MOTOR BICYCLE
BUILDING

WARNING

Remember that the materials and methods described here are from another era. Workers were less safety conscious then, and some methods may be downright dangerous. Be careful! Use good solid judgement in your work, and think ahead. Lindsay Publications Inc. has not tested these methods and materials and does not endorse them. Our job is merely to pass along to you information from another era. Safety is your responsibility.

Write for a complete catalog of unusual books available from:

Lindsay Publications Inc
PO Box 12
Bradley IL 60915-0012

For a fascinating selection of the highest quality books for experimenters, inventors, tinkerers, mad scientists, and a very few normal people...

visit
www.lindsaybks.com

MOTOR BICYCLE
BUILDING

WITH NUMEROUS ENGRAVINGS AND DIAGRAMS

EDITED BY

PAUL N. HASLUCK

EDITOR OF "WORK" AND "BUILDING WORLD"

AUTHOR OF "HANDYBOOKS FOR HANDICRAFTS," ETC. ETC.

CASSELL AND COMPANY, LIMITED

LONDON, PARIS, NEW YORK & MELBOURNE. MCMVI

Motor Bicycle Building

by Paul N. Hasluck

Originally published by
Cassle & Company Ltd
London, New York, Toronto & Melbourne
1906

Reprinted by
Lindsay Publications Inc
Bradley IL 60915   -

ISBN 1-55918-313-6
2004

1   2   3   4   5   6   7

PREFACE.

THIS Handbook contains, in form convenient for everyday use, a number of articles contributed by a cycle and motor maker and expert—Mr. W. Travers —to WORK, one of the weekly journals it is my fortune to edit. The chapter on ignition coils is from the pen of Mr. G. E. Bonney, the well-known writer on practical electrical subjects.

Readers who may desire additional information respecting special details of the matters dealt with, in this Handbook, or instructions on kindred subjects, should address a question to WORK, so that it may be answered in the columns of that journal.

P. N. HASLUCK.

La Belle Sauvage, London.
October, 1906.

CONTENTS.

LIST OF ILLUSTRATIONS.

———◆———

MOTOR BICYCLE BUILDING.

—◆◆◆—

CHAPTER I.

FRAME FOR MOTOR BICYCLE.

In this handbook it is intended fully to describe
the work of building a motor cycle, right from the
pattern making, and not merely to show how to
build it up from a set of purchased fittings. Of
course, where time is a consideration, and where
only one frame is required, it would no doubt
be cheaper to buy a set of standard frame fittings
and put these together; but thousands of workers
possess sufficient skill to make their own patterns,
and to work up the castings, from the instructions
given in this handbook—instructions that will be
specially useful to homeworkers who have more
time than cash to spare, and to small makers and
repairers who may have to construct several
frames during the season. Any reader will be able
to build the frame from a set of finished fittings,
as the design is a standard one. The illustrations
show finished sizes of castings, etc., when machined,
and not the pattern sizes.

To those who have built ordinary cycle frames
(work which is fully described in a companion
handbook, " Cycle Building and Repairing ") no
difficulty should be found in building a frame
for a motor cycle. Much of the work is the same,
and the various fittings differ very little from
those of an ordinary cycle. The tubes and most

of the lugs are certainly heavier and stouter; therefore proper brazing facilities must be at hand. A lamp or blowpipe which is only just powerful enough to braze a light cycle lug will probably fail to braze the rear engine lug, which is somewhat heavy and large, or the rear portion of the bottom bracket, where it is joined to the back fork bridge by the 1⅝-in. tube.

Dimensions.—The two wheels are 28 in. by 2 in. 2¼ in. would be preferable if a powerful engine is fitted, the larger diameter of tyres tending to lessen vibration, thus adding much to the comfort of riding.

The frame measures 2 ft. from the top of the seat lug to the centre of the bracket. This height of frame is suitable for riders not less than 5 ft. 7 in. in height; a rider not more than 5 ft. 6 in. would be better suited with a 23-in. frame. This will mean a corresponding shortening of the head tube (to retain the horizontal position of the top tube) and the front girder tube.

The main-frame tubes are of 1⅛-in. diameter, with head tube 1¼ in.

The back forks and back stays are of D-section, cranked out on the left-hand side of the machine, looking from the back, to give clearance to the belt and belt rim; or patterns can be made for the cranked portion, and malleable castings used for these parts. It will probably be found preferable to use cranked tubes, which can be purchased ready bent, rather than go to the trouble of making patterns for them; these will be lighter and easier to fit up, besides lessening the amount of pattern-making necessary.

The front forks are oval in section, with girder tubes ¾ in. round, swaged down to ½ in. at each end. The front fork tube is of 1⅛-in. diameter, and should be stoutly butted at the crown end to at least No. 13 or No. 14 gauge.

The handle-bar should be of good width, upturned, and brought well back towards the saddle.

This frame is suitable for an engine up to $3\frac{1}{2}$ h.p., this being the largest it is advisable to go to with air cooling. With a $3\frac{1}{2}$-h.p. engine, the frame would be suitable for use with a trailer, side car, or fore car.

Wheels.—The wheels should be built up with No. 12 or No. 13 gauge spokes; if for use with a fore car, the rear wheel should be built of No. 12 gauge at least. The hubs had better be purchased; an Eadie coaster motor hub for the back, and an ordinary motor front hub, with $\frac{3}{8}$-in. spindle, will be suitable. The Eadie hub, with a front wheel rim brake, will give all the braking power required.

Drive.—The drive is by $\frac{3}{4}$-in. V-belt, if for use as a single; or $\frac{7}{8}$-in., or even 1-in., for use with a fore car. The design and position of the engine allows of a good long belt being used. Cranks should be 7-in. throw, and gear low, about 54 in. or 56 in. A suitable engine gear will be a ratio of about $5\frac{1}{2}$ to 1 for all-round work with a trailer or fore car, or as single about 5 to 1—say 4-in. engine pulley with a 20-in. rim pulley. The size of the pulley on the rim must be decided upon before building the frame, to get the proper position of the cranked portion of the back fork and stay. The position as shown in Fig. 1 (p. 13) is intended for a 20-in. rim pulley.

Mud-guards.—Ample mud-guards, $3\frac{1}{2}$ in. wide, should be fitted to both wheels, the rear guard coming through the fork crown and continuing 3 in. or 4 in. below. The front guard will be best fitted in two parts, the front portion extending some 9 in. or 10 in. in front of the crown, and supported by another pair of stays to the front wheel axle, besides being screwed to the front of the crown. These mud-guards stays must be considerably stouter than ordinary cycle stays, and should be made of $\frac{3}{8}$-in. by $\frac{1}{8}$-in. mild steel strip, firmly riveted to guards with copper rivets and washers. Should it be desired to use $2\frac{1}{2}$-in. tyres, the fork crowns, both back and front, should be made $\frac{1}{4}$ in. wider than here designed; and in that case 4-in. mud-guards would be preferable to $3\frac{1}{2}$-in.

Working Drawings.—The first thing to do will be to make a full-size working drawing, as Fig. 1, in chalk, on the wall or floor of the workshop, where it will not be readily rubbed out. Start by marking an horizontal ground line. From a centre 1 ft. 2 in. above this, describe the circle for the rear wheel; 1 ft. $7\frac{1}{2}$ in. from this centre and 11 in. from the ground line will be the bottom bracket centre. Mark off the bracket, and draw in the back forks and fork end, at an angle of 64 degrees. From the back fork draw in the diagonal or down tube, which should be 2 ft. (or less if necessary) from the centre of the bracket. The back stay can then be marked in. Draw the top horizontal tube 2 ft. $7\frac{1}{4}$ in. from the centre line of the down tube to the centre line of the head tube. Fill in the head tube and lugs, after drawing the steering line at the same angle as the down tube; $2\frac{3}{4}$ in. in advance of this steering line and 1 ft. 2 in. from the ground line will be the front wheel hub centre. The bottom front tube can now be drawn in at an angle of 56 degrees from the steering centre. The exact length of this tube will be determined by the size of the crank case of the engine used, but with an engine as shown the length from the centre line of the head to the centre of the $\frac{3}{4}$-in. bolt securing the engine to the lug will be 1 ft. 7 in. The tube and lug from the bottom bracket to the rear engine lug are then drawn in, the distance from the centre of the bracket to the centre of the bolt being $7\frac{1}{2}$ in. The lower horizontal tube will be

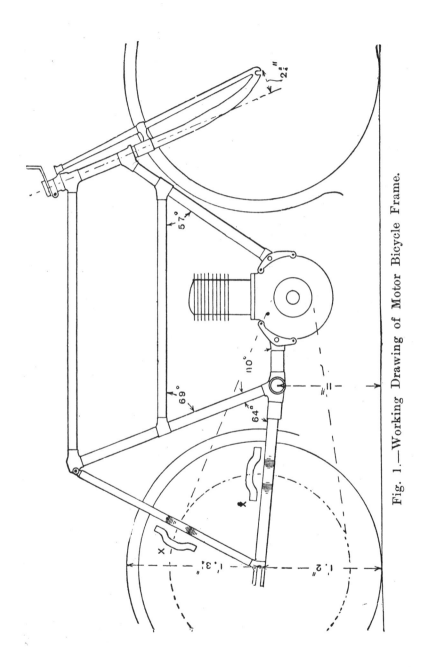

Fig. 1.—Working Drawing of Motor Bicycle Frame.

7¼ in. from the top—that is, 7¼ in. space between the two tubes. The stays which support the centre of the girder tubes are 2 in. from the centre line of the steering tube to the centre of the ¾-in. tubes. The mud-guards are arranged so as to give 1¼-in. clearance from the tyres. With this drawing carefully made, it will be easy to test the various angles of the patterns, and, when building, to see that the various tubes and lugs are accurately fitted together before brazing up.

Tubes.—The following are the sizes of the tubes and the gauge numbers : Top tube, 2 ft. 6¾ in. by 1⅛ in., No. 20; lower horizontal tube, 2 ft. 2¾ in. by 1⅛ in., No. 20; head tube, 6¾ in. by 1¼ in., No. 20; down tube, 1 ft. 11¼ in. by 1⅛ in., No. 20; front tube, 1 ft. 6½ in. by 1⅛ in., No. 14; back stays, D-section, 1 ft. 8½ in., No. 18; back forks, D-section, 1 ft. 1⅜ in., No. 18; back fork crown to bracket, 3 in. by 1⅝ in., No. 20; bracket to rear engine lug, 6¼ by 1⅝ in., No. 20; front forks oval, No. 17 gauge for 28-in. wheel, to give 1¼ in. clearance for tyre; girder tubes (two), 1 ft. 11 in. by ¾ in., No. 18, swaged to ½ in. at each end; steering tube, 11¼ in. by 1⅛ in., No. 16, butted to No. 13 or No. 14; handle-bar, 1 ft. 10 in. wide by 1. in., No. 17, which will take 3 ft. 3 in. of tubing; handle-bar tube, 1 in. by 9 in., No. 16; seat pillar, 8 in. by 1 in., No. 18; top of seat pillar, 5 in. by ⅞ in., No. 16. These lengths will allow for the ends being hollowed out to fit round the connecting parts, a method which greatly strengthens the joints.

Wheel Base, etc.—The wheel base of the machine is 4 ft. 7 in. ; distance from centre of bottom bracket to centre of engine, 1 ft. 0¼ in. ; back fork ends, 5¼ in. wide (to suit Eadie motor coaster hub); front fork ends, 4¼ in. apart.

Tandem Motor Bicycle.—It is not intended here to describe the construction of a tandem, but the work will not present difficulty to a worker who succeeds in making an ordinary motor cycle according to the instructions given in this book. It may be mentioned, however, that the diameter of the tubes for a tandem motor bicycle with lady's frame at back will be regulated by the make and type of fittings used, but the gauges should be as follows : Bottom front tube, No. 14; down tubes, No. 18; top and bottom horizontal tubes, No. 20; head tube, No. 20; bottom bracket connecting tubes, if $\frac{7}{8}$-in. twin, No. 16, if $1\frac{1}{2}$-in. single tube, No. 18; rear forks, No. 16; rear stays, No. 20; front forks, No. 17, with No. 18 girder stays; steering tube, No. 16, butted 12 at the crown. Chater Lea and Co. make several designs of tandem fittings that would be suitable for the purpose.

CHAPTER II.

PATTERNS FOR FRAME CASTINGS.

Introduction.—The method of turning out the patterns will now be considered. As making the coreboxes for some of the patterns will probably be the most difficult part of the work, these will be dispensed with as much as possible, and plain prints and cores used whenever practicable. If a number of sets have to be made from the patterns, it would be advisable to make proper core-boxes for those particular patterns requiring them.

Wood for Patterns.—One of the best woods to use for the patterns is mahogany, but well-seasoned white pine is cheaper, and easier to work, and this, if well varnished, will stand a few sets of castings being made from them.

Bottom Bracket.—Fig. 2 is a side view of the bottom bracket; for this, plain prints and cores may be used. Turn up the body part, which is $3\frac{1}{2}$ in. long by $1\frac{5}{8}$ in. in diameter, finished casting, making due allowance for shrinkage and machining. As only the two end faces of the outside of the casting will be machined, $\frac{1}{16}$ in. for machining, and another $\frac{1}{16}$ in. for shrinkage, should be allowed. It is usual to allow about $\frac{3}{16}$ in. to the foot for shrinkage, but with these small castings, where the length does not exceed 2 in. or 3 in., it will generally be found that what is lost by shrinkage is made up by the moulder " rapping " the pattern in the sand, so that as a rule it will scarcely be worth while to take shrinkage into consideration. In turning up the body part of the bracket leave a core-print at each end, $\frac{1}{2}$ in.

long by $1\frac{5}{16}$ in. in diameter, rounding off the ends slightly, so that the pattern will leave the sand easily.

Now turn up the three tube members to take tne rear and front $1\frac{5}{8}$-in. tubes and the $1\frac{1}{8}$-in. down tube. These members, when the castings are machined, should be $\frac{1}{16}$ in. larger in diameter at the extreme thin edge than the bore, and at the root, where they join the body part, quite $\frac{3}{16}$ in. larger than the bore; this gives a taper to the lug of about 3 degrees. The core-prints for those members must be longer by about $\frac{1}{4}$ in. than the depth the core is to go in the pattern, so that it

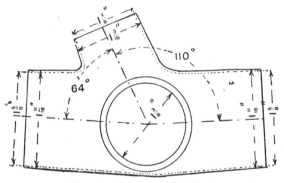

Fig. 2.—Bottom Bracket.

may balance in the mould, being supported at the one end only, and not at both ends, as is the body core. The length of the $1\frac{5}{8}$-in. members will be 2 in. from the centre of the bracket, and the $1\frac{1}{8}$-in. members $1\frac{3}{4}$-in. from the centre. The core-prints will be $1\frac{5}{8}$ in. and $1\frac{3}{8}$ in. long respectively, and $\frac{1}{8}$ in. smaller in diameter than the size of the finished bores for the tubes. These three members must be hollowed out at the ends, and fitted together on to the body part at the angles shown in Fig. 2, and then tested for accuracy on the full-size drawing before being finally glued and pegged on. All three members are fitted centrally

to the body.   There must be no sharp angles where
the various parts join; the joints should be
rounded and smoothed off neatly.   To one not
used to this class of work, some difficulty will
be found in doing it neatly, in which case sharp
corners may be filled up with good hard wax,
applied hot and smoothed off when cold.   Care
must be taken that all three members are at right

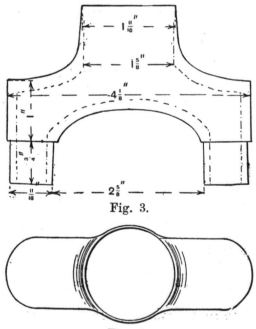

Fig. 3.

Fig. 4.

Figs. 3 and 4.—Back Fork Crown.

angles to the body part.   No provision has been
made on this pattern for securing the bracket
cups in position, as it is intended that these
should be made extra wide, and fitted with lock-
nuts to lock against the faces of the bracket.
Alternative methods would be to provide a lug
at each end for a locking cotter pin and nut, as
in the B.S.A. and other brackets; or to fit a

small set-pin and nut to press on to the bracket discs—in this case the thickness of the bracket shell would have to be increased by fitting a small circular piece, about $\frac{3}{16}$ in. thick, on to each end of the pattern, so that a good thread may be tapped in for the set pin. In adopting either of these alternative methods, the ordinary standard bracket discs may be used.

Back Fork Crown.—The back fork crown (Figs. 3 and 4) is a pattern for which it will be necessary to make a core-box, as the coring necessary is not straight and circular, like the bracket, but irregular in formation. The pattern should be made in four pieces—the turned part for the $1\frac{5}{8}$-in. tube, the body, and the two end pieces for the back forks. The turned part will be the same as the two large ends of the

Fig. 5.—End of Back Fork Crown.

bottom bracket, except that the print will need to be only $\frac{1}{2}$ in. or $\frac{5}{8}$ in. long, as the core will be supported in the mould at two other points, namely, the two D-section parts of the back fork lugs. The body part will be made with the grain running across the pattern. After the top part has been roughly turned and the body cut roughly to shape, the top may be let into the body and glued up; then again returned to the lathe, and the junction of the two and the top of the shoulders turned to shape as far as possible. The two D-section ends are afterwards cut to shape as in Fig. 5, and dowelled and glued on. The width of the crown over all is $4\frac{1}{2}$ in., and the inside width between the fork lugs $2\frac{5}{8}$ in. The finished size of these fork lugs (D-section) is $1\frac{1}{16}$ in. by $\frac{11}{16}$ in., and the core-prints should be the same sec-

tion, $1\frac{3}{16}$ in. by $\frac{7}{16}$ in., and $\frac{3}{4}$ in. long. The core-box
is made in halves dowelled together, and must
be carved out so that a uniform thickness of
metal, about $\frac{1}{8}$ in., is left all over the casting.
It will require accurate work. The prints on the
pattern must fit the core-box accurately when
closed up. The two D-section prints must fit into
the D ends of the core-box, and the $1\frac{9}{16}$-in. print
must fit the other end of the core-box. The over-
all length of the box is the same as the over-all
length of the pattern (over the end of the prints),
so that the core made in the box will drop snugly
into the impression left in the sand by the pat-

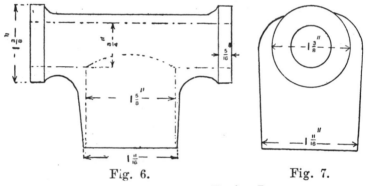

Fig. 6.   Fig. 7.

Figs. 6 and 7.—Rear Engine Lug.

tern. In turning the top part of the pattern,
leave the end rounded, so that it may come away
from the sand easily, and also chamfer off the
two ends of the D prints for the same reason.

Engine Lugs.—The rear engine lug is shown
in front elevation at Fig. 6 and in end view at
Fig. 7, similar views of the front engine lug being
given at Figs. 8 and 9. The rear lug is made in two
pieces, and no core-box is required. The body
part is turned to the dimensions given in the
illustrations, due allowance being made for facing
up the ends. The core-print on each end will
be $\frac{5}{8}$ in. in diameter by $\frac{3}{4}$ in. long. The right-

angle member to take the 1⅝-in. tube will be the same as the large members on the bracket pattern, the same instructions also applying as regards the filling up sharp corners and the length of the core-print to balance the core in the mould. The front engine lug is the same as the rear engine lug, only the right-angle member is to receive 1⅛-in. tubing instead of 1⅝-in., and must be made smaller to correspond.

Rear Fork Ends.—Fig. 10 shows one of the rear fork ends (left-hand side), Fig. 11 being an end view to show the section. This pattern may

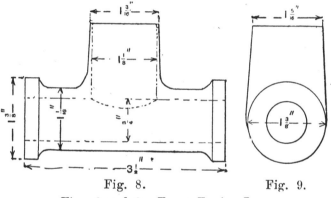

Fig. 8.   Fig. 9.

Figs. 8 and 9.—Front Engine Lug.

be made in two pieces, the main part being a piece of 3 3/16 in. by 1 3/16 in. by ⅞ in., the grain running with the length. The slot for the spindle should be made 1½ in. by 7/16 in. full, or ½ in. bare, to allow filing out to ½ in. in the casting. The D-section end for the back fork is 1 1/16 in. by 11/16 in., the same as the ends of the back fork crown (see Fig. 5). The top portion, for the top backstay, is made from a separate piece, and is dovetailed and glued on, the D being 15/16 in. by 9/16 in. finished size (see Fig. 12). The centre of both D portions is cut out for lightness. The fork end is 5/32 in. thick, the raised portion being

formed by cutting out to shape two thin slips
of wood and gluing in place, making the combined thickness at this part $\frac{1}{4}$ in. The ends may
be left square or rounded, as shown in the end
view, Fig. 11, to receive the chain adjusters. It
will be necessary to make another pattern to pair
with this, for the right-hand side, unless the top
portion is made detachable, so that it can be
fitted on to the other side of the pattern to form

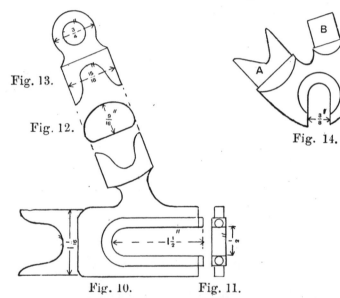

Fig. 13.

Fig. 12.

Fig. 14.

Fig. 10.   Fig. 11.

Figs. 10 and 11.—Left-hand Fork End.   Fig. 12.—Top
Member of Left-hand Fork End.   Fig. 13.—Back Stay
Eye.   Fig. 14.—Front Fork End.

the right-hand fork end. The square edges of
both outside and inside slots should be chamfered
off to leave the sand, also the centre of the D
parts where it is hollowed out.

Top Stay Eye.—The top stay eye is shown at
Fig. 13. It is of D-section, and of the same
dimensions as the top part of the fork end (see
Fig. 12). The round end is $\frac{3}{4}$ in. by $\frac{3}{16}$ in. thick,
with the hole $\frac{3}{8}$ in. finished sizes. Two of these

castings will be required, but, being exactly alike, only one pattern is necessary.

Front Fork Ends.—Two front fork ends (Fig. 14) will be required, but as there is so little difference in their construction, one pattern may be used for both. The only difference in the finished fork ends is the angle of the two projections with the flat face; as this angle is so small (about

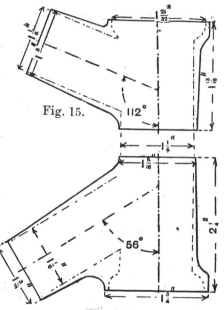

Fig. 15.

Fig. 16.

Figs. 15 and 16.—Patterns for Top and Bottom Head Lugs.

3 or 4 degrees), it can be obtained by making the pattern with no angle and bending the casting to suit. The pattern may be cut from a single piece. The flat portion (to take the wheel spindle) is $\frac{1}{4}$ in. thick, the $\frac{3}{4}$-in. circular portion, which is recessed $\frac{1}{16}$ in. deep, being left to be done on the casting. The slot is $\frac{3}{8}$ in. wide, but it will be better to leave this part solid, and either saw or file out the slot after the $\frac{3}{8}$-in. hole and the $\frac{3}{4}$-in.

recess have been machined in the casting. The part A is oval in shape, $\frac{3}{4}$ in. by $\frac{3}{8}$ in., to receive the bottom of the oval front fork; and the round portion B is $\frac{3}{8}$ in. in diameter, to receive the lower end of the girder tube. The angle of these two lugs will be best obtained from the full-size drawing.

Top and Bottom Head Lugs.—The top and bottom head lugs (Figs. 15 and 16) are very similar patterns, the only difference being in the angle and the increased length of the bottom lug. They are each made from two turned parts, glued and pegged together at the angles shown, 112 degrees for the top lug and 56 degrees for the

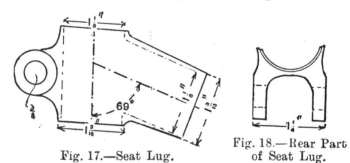

Fig. 17.—Seat Lug.

Fig. 18.—Rear Part of Seat Lug.

bottom lug. Both these patterns should have a core-box to get the cored part as shown by the dotted lines, in which case the print at the large end would be $1\frac{19}{32}$ in. in diameter by $\frac{1}{2}$ in. long; this would be allowing $\frac{1}{16}$ in. for finishing the casting to $1\frac{21}{32}$ in. inside at the end. The diameter of the prints at the other two ends is $1\frac{1}{16}$ in. and $1\frac{3}{16}$ in. by $\frac{1}{2}$ in. long. If it is decided to do without core-boxes for these two patterns, the larger part will have to be plain-cored right through $1\frac{3}{16}$ in., leaving the recessed portion for the ball-race to be machined out of the casting. The diameter of the print for the $1\frac{1}{8}$-in. tubes is the same as for the core-boxes, but the length is different. The core being supported in the mould at one end only, the print must be longer on the pattern than the depth to be cored. Thus the print for the top head lug should be $1\frac{1}{2}$ in. long, and that for the bottom $1\frac{7}{8}$ in. long.

Seat Lug.—The seat lug (Fig. 17) is made from two turned parts; the rear part, to take the $\frac{3}{8}$-in. bolt, is cut out by hand, similar in shape to Fig. 18, and glued and pegged on. Turn the centre part for the down tube $1\frac{5}{16}$ in. in diameter in the centre, tapering to $1\frac{3}{16}$ in. at each end by $1\frac{5}{8}$ in. long, the print standing out $\frac{1}{2}$ in. at each end by $1\frac{1}{16}$ in. in diameter. The front portion for the top tube is $1\frac{3}{16}$ in. in diameter at the extreme

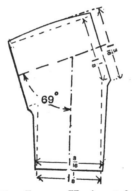

Fig. 19.—Lower Horizontal Lug.

edge, tapering up at about 3 degrees of taper. The core-print for this member is $1\frac{1}{16}$ in. in diameter by $1\frac{3}{8}$ in. long. The rear part is cored out $\frac{3}{8}$ in., as shown by the dotted lines in Fig. 18, and will require a print of this diameter, standing out $\frac{1}{2}$ in. at each end.

Lower Horizontal Lugs.—The patterns for the two lower horizontal lugs (Fig. 19) are alike except in the angle, the one shown being 69 degrees and the other 57 degrees. They are made from two turned parts, and each member is to take $1\frac{1}{8}$-in. tube. The parts are exactly as the main parts of the seat lug, the only difference being the absence of the rear ears and the different angle of the front lug—that is, 57 degrees. The same remarks apply with regard to the core-prints.

Girder Tube Lugs.—Figs. 20 and 21 are side and top views of one of the girder tube lugs. A pair of these will be required, but the difference is so slight that one pattern may be used for both. This pattern should be made with the grain of the wood running with the length of the pattern, and the prints glued and pegged on each side. The drawings give all dimensions, which are

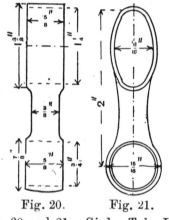

Fig. 20.   Fig. 21.

Figs. 20 and 21.—Girder Tube Lugs.

finished sizes of the machined casting, so due allowance must be made for machining. The core and print for the oval part should be made as near the finished size as possible, as this has to be filed out in the casting. It will be necessary to have a core-box for the oval part; a piece of fork tube of this size and section will answer admirably. The length of prints for both oval and round holes need be only ½ in. from each side of the pattern.

Front Fork Crown.—The pattern for the front fork crown is shown in top and front view by

Figs. 22 and 23. It may be made from one piece, with the prints for the central core and two oval cores glued and pegged on. It is $4\frac{5}{8}$ in. over all, $1\frac{5}{8}$ in. deep at the ends, where the forks fit, and $1\frac{1}{8}$ in. deep in the centre. The central core-print is $1\frac{1}{16}$ in. in diameter, and the ovals, indicated by dotted lines in Fig. 22, $1\frac{1}{4}$ in. by $\frac{11}{16}$ in.; that is the full finished size, and owing to the awkwardness of cleaning out these in the casting, it will be advisable to core them out full size, or very

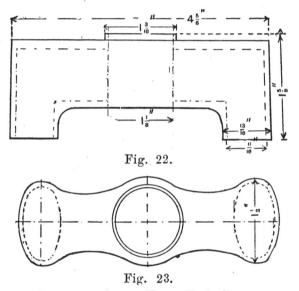

Fig. 22.

Fig. 23.

Figs. 22 and 23.—Front Fork Crown.

nearly full size. A core-box will be necessary for this pattern, allowing for a uniform thickness of $\frac{1}{8}$ in. in the casting, as shown by the dotted lines in Fig. 23, except at the edges of the oval openings, which may be a bare $\frac{3}{32}$ in. It will be noticed that a ring or collar is shown on top of the crown; this is for the bottom ball-race to fit on. The core-prints need only project $\frac{5}{8}$ in., as the core will be supported at four points.

Ball-head or Steering Tube Lug.—The ball-

head, or steering tube lug, is shown by Figs. 24
and 25, these being side and bottom views. It is
made by turning the main part to the dimensions
given, allowing for machining. The central core-
print is $1\frac{1}{16}$ in., projecting $\frac{5}{8}$ in. at each end. The
rear part for the $\frac{3}{8}$-in. bolt is cut out separately,
and glued and pegged on. It is $1\frac{1}{4}$ in. wide, and
has a $\frac{3}{8}$-in. core-print. The two projections to

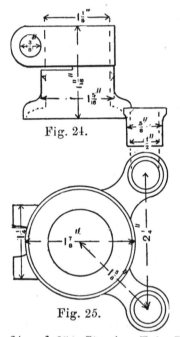

Fig. 24.

Fig. 25.

Figs. 24 and 25.—Steering Tube Lug.

receive the ends of the girder tubes are cut out
to shape as in Fig. 25, length with the grain, and
the two lugs turned to shape and glued and pegged
on. The prints are $\frac{7}{16}$ in. in diameter by $\frac{3}{4}$ in.
long. The two projecting pieces being so light
(only $\frac{3}{16}$ in. thick), they should be dovetailed into
the main part of the pattern, as well as glued and
pegged, or they may soon be broken off at the
foundry.

Engine Plates.—The pattern for the engine plates is shown by Figs. 26 and 27, which are side and end views. Four of these plates will be required. They may be cast in malleable iron from a pattern, but it is better to have them forged from mild steel. Should castings, however, be used, have only the large centre hole cored, leaving the ends solid to be drilled out in the casting.

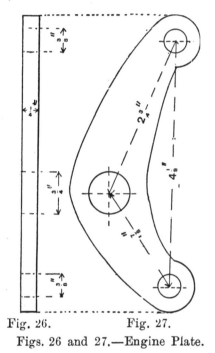

Fig. 26.   Fig. 27.

Figs. 26 and 27.—Engine Plate.

This also applies if forgings are used, as the exact position of these holes can only be ascertained when the frame is built and the engine tried in the frame, with wheels in position.

"*Leave*" *on Patterns.*—This is all the pattern-making that will be necessary, and it only remains to get the required number of castings made from them at a good malleable iron foundry. All parts of the patterns must be nicely smoothed off with fine glasspaper, leaving no rough edges or parts, and care must be observed to impart sufficient "leave" to the various parts requiring it. What is meant by "leave" on a pattern will be understood by taking, first, a solid ball and then a solid square as patterns. The ball would be moulded half in each moulding box, the parting taking place exactly at the centre of the pattern; thus, as all parts of this pattern slope away from the centre or parting line, no "leave" would be necessary, as this would be a perfect form for leaving the sand well. But if a solid square or cube is taken, some part of the pattern would have to be tapered off to enable the pattern to come away from the sand without breaking down some part of the impression, unless the pattern was moulded with a corner of the square uppermost, and the parting takes place at a point which embraces four corners. Whatever other position this pattern might be moulded in, some portions of the flat sides would have to be tapered off from the parting line to enable it to leave properly. It is only necessary to look at a pattern carefully and imagine which will be the most convenient position to mould it in, to see what parts require "leave."

Painting Core-prints, etc.—All core-prints should be painted black—a little vegetable black mixed with varnish will do—and the whole pattern given two coats of shellac varnish. This varnish can be easily made by dissolving brown shellac in methylated spirit, shaking the bottle frequently. Heat will assist it to dissolve, but great care must be taken, as the spirit is very inflammable, and likely to cause an accident if taken too near a light. The inside of the core-boxes should also be given two good coats of shellac varnish when finished.

Making Plain Round Cores.—For making the

plain round cores, nothing beats cycle tube, and pieces of this to fit the various prints should be selected and cut to the required lengths. Where the junction of two cores is at an angle, such as the head lugs, seat lug, and lower horizontal tube lugs, the core tubes should be cut off at a corresponding angle, and also hollowed out at the angle end, so that the coring may extend as far as possible.

Oval Cores.—For the oval cores also pieces of fork blade of the proper section will do perfectly for making the cores, and will save a deal of trouble in core-box making.

Dowelling Halves of Core-boxes.—The two halves of the core-boxes for fork crowns, or whatever core-boxes that are made in halves, should be fitted with two or three dowels to ensure the halves closing perfectly accurate; they should fit easily, but without shake. Small brass pegs and sockets can be purchased for the purpose, and where the boxes are likely to be used much it is advisable to fit these, as the wood dowels soon wear with much usage.

Metal Patterns.—Where a large number of castings are to be made from one pattern, metal patterns, preferably brass, are made, and cast-iron core-boxes used.

Dimensions on Illustrations.—It must be borne in mind that all dimensions given in the illustrations included in this chapter are finished sizes of castings, and due allowance must be made for machining.

CHAPTER III.

BUILDING FRAME FROM CASTINGS.

HAVING received the castings from the foundry, free them well from sand ; and should any castings have become distorted in the annealing process, correct this by careful hammering.

Bottom Bracket.—The bottom bracket may first be taken in hand. Chuck the casting in a jaw chuck, and bore out the centre part $1\frac{7}{16}$ in. in diameter, leaving $\frac{5}{8}$ in. at each end a full $1\frac{5}{16}$ in. to screw $1\frac{3}{8}$ in. by 24 threads. Face off the end standing out from the chuck at this setting ; the other end should be faced off on a screwed mandrel to get perfect truth ; but if carefully chucked, it may be faced fairly true by this means. The bracket cups should be obtained or made previous to screwing the bracket, so that they may be tried in to fit before removing the casting from the chuck. The cups should be a good tight fit, so that they can only just be screwed up with a peg wrench. The width of the bracket when finished should be $3\frac{1}{2}$ in.

Boring the Three Tube Lugs.—The best way to bore the three tube lugs will be on an angle plate or an upright drilling machine ; but if such a tool is not available, the lathe will do, either by bolting the angle plate to the face plate, or by holding the casting in the jaw chuck. If the latter method is adopted, greater care will be necessary in seeing that the holes are bored at perfect right angles to the centre bore. With a true angle plate and the ends of the casting faced true, this will be ensured. The front member, to take the tube from the back fork crown, will be bored $1\frac{5}{8}$

in. right through into the centre, and the outside
trued up. The lug to take the down tube will now
be bored 1⅛ in. right through, and at an angle of
110 degrees with the first boring. The rear lug
is bored 1⅝ in. at an angle of 64 degrees with the
last boring. The various tubes should be tried in
their places before the casting is shifted, and
should be a good tight push fit in their holes.
Holes for lubricators should be drilled ¾ in. from
each face, in such a position that the lubricators
will be upright when the bracket is in position.
If lugs for set pins, by which the cups or discs are
to be locked, have been provided, these should be
drilled and tapped to suit the set pins. The
dimensions of the disc to be used with lock-nuts,
and also of the bracket axle, will be given later.

Back Fork Crown.—The back fork crown casting should be chucked in the jaw chuck and bored
1⅝ in., as deep as possible, and the edges trued
up ; or the ends of the D-section projections may
be levelled off and the casting stripped to the face
plate to bore this 1⅝ in. hole. Whichever method
is adopted, care must be taken to get the hole
perfectly true with the D ends.

Engine Lugs.—The engine lugs should be
chucked true, and the ¾-in. holes bored right
through and reamered, the faces being turned up
on a mandrel. They should measure 3½ in. over
all when finished. The tube lugs should then be
bored 1⅛ in. and 1⅝ in. respectively, and the edges
trued up.

Front Fork Ends.—The castings of the front
fork ends will require very little machining. The
⅜-in. hole will require drilling, and the ¾-in. recess
should be machined in the outside face of each
with a peg drill or cutter. The slot can then be
filed out to meet the ⅜-in. hole. The ⅜-in. lug to
take the bottom end of the girder tube can be
turned or filed as preferred. As this is a rather
awkward casting to chuck, it may be advisable to

file this to fit the tube at the same time as the
oval lug is filed to fit the lower end of the oval
fork blade. Whilst these are being fitted to their
respective tubes, they should be tried on the full-
size drawing to see that the angle is correct. The
two stay eyes will require drilling out $\frac{3}{8}$ in. ; these
may be drilled at the same time as any of the
other $\frac{3}{8}$-in. holes.

Head Lugs.—Chuck the head lugs in the jaw
chuck, large end outwards ; bore through $1\frac{1}{4}$ in.
to fit the head tube, and turn out the recess for
ball-races, as shown by the dotted lines in Figs.
15 and 16 (p. 23). These recesses will measure
$\frac{21}{32}$ in. at the extreme ends by $\frac{5}{16}$ in. deep. Face
off the ends, and true up the outer edges. The
$1\frac{1}{8}$-in. tube members may be bored whilst held in
the jaw chuck or on the angle plate, tilted to the
correct angle—112 degrees for the top head lug
and 56 degrees for the bottom one.

Seat Lug.—Chuck the seat-lug casting in the
jaw chuck to bore out the central $1\frac{1}{8}$-in. hole, with
the top end outwards ; re-chuck or fix on the angle
plate, to bore out the $1\frac{1}{8}$-in. hole for the front
tube. The rear part will have to be drilled out
$\frac{3}{8}$ in., and the ears faced off true for the back-stay
eyes to bed against. The saw-cut should be put in
the back, midway between the ears, before the lug
is fitted and brazed to the seat tube, as the casting
becomes very hard and difficult to saw after it has
been brazed.

Lower Horizontal Tube Lugs.—The treatment
of the lower horizontal tube lugs is the same as
that of the seat lug ; but note should be taken of
the difference in the angle.

Drilling Girder Tube Stays.—The $\frac{3}{4}$-in. hole in
each of the girder tube stays may be bored on the
drilling machine or the lathe. In setting these
castings for boring the $\frac{3}{4}$-in. hole, due allowance
should be made for the difference in parallel between this and the oval hole. On reference to the

full-size drawing, it will be noticed that the girder
tubes approach nearer to the centre steering line
as they reach the top of the head. Also, looking
from the front of the machine, it will be seen that
the two tubes are closer together at the top than
they are at the fork crown. If this difference is
allowed for when drilling the $\frac{3}{4}$-in. holes, it will
not be necessary to bend the tubes to bring them
into place. Knocking these lugs on a $\frac{3}{4}$-in. mandrel, after they are drilled and the edges trued up
in the lathe, will add greatly to their appearance.
The oval holes must be filed out to fit the fork
blades.

Front Fork Crown.—The front fork crown may
be held in the jaw chuck or strapped to the face-
plate, the centre hole bored $1\frac{1}{8}$ in., and the top
faced off and the shoulder turned $1\frac{3}{16}$ in. in
diameter by $\frac{1}{8}$ in. deep. If the casting is being
machined, strapped to the face-plate, this latter
operation will have to be done on a mandrel between the centres. The oval-section holes will
have to be filed or scraped out for the fork blades
to fit. While the casting is on the mandrel in the
lathe, the ends of the ovals may be faced off true.

.Steering-tube Lug Casting.—Chuck the steering-tube lug casting bottom or large end outwards,
bore through $1\frac{1}{8}$ in. to fit the steering tube (a tight
hand fit), and recess out the part shown dotted in
Figs. 24 and 25 (p. 28) to take the ball-race.
This will be of the same size across as the recesses
in the head lugs, but $\frac{1}{32}$ in. deeper, so that the
edge of the casting may overlap the outer edge
of the top ball head lug when the two are brought
together with the balls in place. This hides the
balls, and keeps the bearing more or less dust-
proof. The bottom ball head lug should be made
to overlap the bottom ball-race on the fork crown
in the same manner for the same purpose. At
this chucking, the under side of the front ears
may be faced, as well as the edges of the two

girder tube lugs, on a mandrel in the lathe centres; the outside and top of the casting may be turned up, or as much of the outside as the projections will allow. The ears should be drilled out $\frac{3}{8}$ in., and faced on both sides with a facing cutter; the cutter that was used for recessing the front fork ends will do for this also. The two $\frac{1}{3}$-in. holes for the girder tubes must now be drilled, and finished out with a bottoming drill or cutter, so that the holes have square corners or a flat bottom. A fine saw-cut should be made nearly half through the casting, just under the ears, as shown in Fig. 24 (p. 28), and a broader cut should be run down to meet this midway between the ears.

Engine Plates.—The four engine-plate castings should be levelled, the $\frac{3}{4}$-in. holes drilled square with the face, the sides smoothed, and the edges filed up. One of the $\frac{3}{8}$-in. holes in each plate may be marked off and drilled, leaving the other $\frac{3}{8}$-in. holes to be marked off and drilled after the frame is built up and the engine is in position.

Ball-races.—It will now be necessary to make the ball-races (Figs. 28 and 29, p. 37). Four of these will be required—three, as illustrated, for the steering tube lug and the top and bottom head lugs, and one for the fork crown; this last will have square corners instead of round, and a $1\frac{3}{16}$-in. hole to fit the shoulder on the fork crown, the outside diameter being $1\frac{21}{32}$ in. These are rather awkward to make in an ordinary lathe; to get them true they are made on a large hollow mandrel lathe from the bar. It would be as well to buy these ready-made, as they do not cost much. If it is decided to make them, good mild steel, well case-hardened, should be used. It would be simpler, in making the steering bearings, to dispense with cups or loose ball-races altogether, and turn the ball-races in the head and steering lugs themselves, with a steel cone only to fit on the fork crown. In this case the bearings should be two-point bearings, and not four-point, as shown with the loose ball-races. These parts will not be so durable as well-hardened steel ball-races; but if balls not less than $\frac{3}{16}$ in., or $\frac{3}{16}$ in. for the top bearing and $\frac{7}{32}$ in. for the bottom bearing, are used, they will wear very well. The malleable-iron castings become very hard when they are brazed, and thus stand a lot of wear. The loose steel cone on the head will, of course, be well hardened, and the radius of the bearing curves should not be much greater than the radius of the ball used, thus giving a good large bearing surface, instead of the small bearing surface usual with **V**-groove

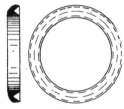

Fig. 28.   Fig 29.

Figs. 28 and 29.—Ball-race.

bearing discs. One advantage of the absence of loose ball-race bearings is that there are no separate parts to get loose and cause play in the head.

Bottom Bracket Axle.—Fig. 30 gives the full dimensions for the bottom bracket axle, which should be made, preferably, from one of Leadbeater & Scott's patent stampings. These have a dead soft centre, which will not harden, with an exterior covering of a carbon steel that will harden direct in water, and gives a very hard wearing surface. Failing one of these stampings, cast steel should be used, carefully hardened at the wearing parts only. Mild steel, case-hardened, does very well for this job if proper facilities are at hand for pot-hardening; but using mild

steel, and attempting to harden by the ordinary
means on the open hearth with potash, etc., is
quite useless. In making this axle, cut off the steel
or stamping just the dead lengths required before
drilling up the ends, so that the centres upon
which the axle is turned may be left in, to true it
up by after hardening. Fit the cranks and file the
keyways before hardening. Special wide bracket
discs are used with this axle, as shown at A, lock-
nuts (Figs. 31 and 32) securing them. If it has
been decided to lock these discs by set pins or
transverse cotters, the ordinary standard pattern
discs, which can be purchased for about 6d. each,
will do. Should lock-nuts for the bracket discs be

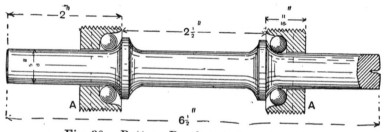

Fig. 30.—Bottom Bracket Axle in Position.

necessary, they may be made from ordinary gas
back-nuts, bored out and re-screwed, if suitable
stampings are not available; or, if the latter are
used, they can be made from stout 1-in. washers,
bored and screwed. They need not be filed up or
shaped hexagon; but a couple of deep notches
may be filed in their edge for adjustment purposes, as shown in Figs. 31 and 32. They should
be 1⅜ in. by 24 threads, the same as the discs,
but must be a somewhat easier fit on the discs
than the discs are in the bracket, otherwise difficulty will be experienced in adjusting the bearing
properly. At least one face of the nuts must be
trued up with the thread.

Fitting Lock-nut to Steering Tube.—The steering tube must be screwed at one end with a fine thread for ¾ in. down. A coarser thread than 26 to the inch should not be used, otherwise the tube would be weakened by the depth of the thread. A lock-nut to fit this will be required, and the remarks made with reference to the bracket locknuts apply also to this. Whilst screwing the steering tube and fitting the nut, pay attention to the fitting of the steering-tube lug, which must be a good sliding fit without shake. The saw-cut, which allows the tube to be tightened on to the

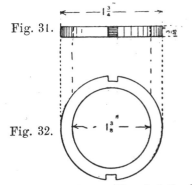

Figs. 31 and 32.—Bracket Lock-nut.

handle-bar stem, should not be made until the handle-bar has been fitted in the tube.

Engine Bolts.—Two ¾-in. turned engine bolts (Fig. 33) will be required for securing the engine plates to their lugs. These are turned from 1⅛-in. mild steel, one to the dimensions given in the illustration, and the other ¼ in. shorter. They should be a good push fit, without shake, in the ¾-in. holes of the engine plates and the lugs on the frame.

Building up Frame.—All the lugs and parts having been machined ready for fitting up to the various tubes, the rear part of the frame may now be built up. Cut off the back forks to the exact length required; clean out the ends where the fork ends and fork crown ends fit; level off the ends where the fork ends fit; and chamfer off the inner edge of the D tubes, so that they fit neatly up to the shoulders. If these fit tight, they need not be pegged for brazing. Fit the top stay eyes into the top back stays in a similar way. Cut a small notch in the bottom of the $\frac{3}{8}$-in. hole in one of these stay eyes, so that a small peg fitted under the head of the bolt, which holds the seat pillar tight, may engage with this slot and so prevent the bolt from turning while the nut is being tightened or undone. Before fitting up the fork ends and stay eyes, or cutting the tubes at all, see that the cranked portion of these comes in the proper position to allow of the belt rim clearing properly, and on the left-hand side of the machine. These four joints are then brazed and filed up.

Setting Rear Fork Ends.—The fork ends should now be set on the wheel. (The wheels should be made or procured before starting to build the frame.) To set the fork ends, tighten up in their place on the wheel spindle and set until the other ends of the forks are the proper distance apart, to correspond with the D-section ends of the fork crown, and at an equal distance from the edge of the wheel rim. It is better not to set these in their place on the spindle, or the latter may get bent with the strain; they should be removed to the vice to be bent to the required angle.

Brazing Tubes to Bottom Bracket.—The two short pieces of $1\frac{5}{8}$-in. tube may now be fitted to the bracket, and also the down tube, after thoroughly cleaning out the various lugs and the ends of the tubes. The ends of the $1\frac{5}{8}$-in. tube that fit into the bracket should be hollowed out, to allow of the tubes fitting well up into the bracket. The back fork crown is then fitted to the other end of the $1\frac{5}{8}$-in. tube. Now try this

part on the working drawing, and see that all
the measurements and the angle of the down tube
are correct. Before pegging these joints and brazing up, make sure of the following points : The
down tube must be at right angles to the bore
of the bracket ; test this with a steel straightedge
on the trued-up faces. See that the back fork
crown is square with the down tube ; test this by
placing the straightedge on the top of the D-section ears and sighting it from the back, when the
straightedge should appear at right angles to the
down tube. Some blacklead mixed with oil should
be rubbed into the threaded ends of the bracket,
and also into the tapped lubricator holes, to prevent the brass and borax adhering to these parts.

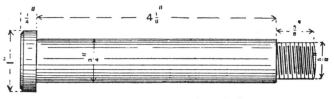

Fig. 33.—Engine Plate Bolt.

These four joints will require careful brazing, and
a good blast to obtain sufficient heat. The best
way to proceed is to direct the blast on to the
heavy portion of the front lug ; get this well
heated up, and make the front 1⅝-in. joint. Now
shift the flame on to the root of the 1⅛-in. lug, and
braze this joint ; then on to the heavy part of the
rear 1⅝-in. lug, and finish this joint.
    It will be advisable next to remove the job
from the hearth and thoroughly brush these joints,
while well hot, with the wire brazing brush. The
joint of the rear 1⅝-in. tube with the back fork
crown can then be finally brazed. Brazing this
last joint will scale the D ends of the crown, and
these must therefore be cleaned up again before
fitting the back forks. Small air-holes must be

drilled on the inside of these back forks before filing up and brazing. Other tubes requiring air-holes for brazing will be the back stays, lower horizontal tube, and front forks; and the top tube and bottom front tube as well, unless the ends of these are opened out into their lugs. When the back forks, exactly equal in length, are finally fitted to the crown, remove and load each tube with brass and borax, knock the joints well home, and peg securely. Fix a stay or strut between the two fork ends, so that they will be held the same distance apart as they will be when the wheel is in position. In the absence of a suitable stay, the hub spindle will do, the cones and nuts being used to keep the fork ends the correct distance apart and the faces square with each other. Shake the charge, placed inside the tubes, well down towards the joints, and braze one at a time, with the fork on its side.

Fitting Ball-head.—Fit up the ball-head tube to the top and bottom head lugs, the top tube to the top head lug, and the bottom front tube to the bottom head lug, and peg the joints. The ends of the tubes should be hollowed out to fit up against the head tube. Before brazing, see that the three tubes are in one plane; to test this, place a long straightedge across the ends of the top and bottom tubes, and sight this with the ball-head tube. Also see that the ends of the tubes are the proper distance apart to drop into place with the seat lug and front engine lug on the drawing. While these joints are hot, scrape out the ends of the ball-head lugs, where the ball races fit; this will save a lot of work after, if any brass has stuck to these parts. Mark off, on the down and bottom tubes, the position that the lower horizontal tube lugs will occupy, and clean the tubes at these parts. Slip the two lugs on to the down and bottom tubes before the seat lug or the front engine lug is fitted to its tube.

Fitting Front to Rear Parts.—The seat lug can now be fitted to the top tube, and the lower horizontal tube to its lugs, and the front and rear portions of the frame connected together by fitting the seat lug on to the top of the down tube. In fitting this front portion to the rear part, see that all the tubes lie in one plane before pegging up. To test this, place a long straightedge across each side of the ball-head and down tubes; the end of this should fall at an equal distance from each fork-end face. The ball-head tube must also be perfectly parallel with the down tube.

These three joints may now be brazed up. The top tube is opened out into the seat lug by punching a hole through the down tube inside the seat lug. This will act as an air hole, and serve as a means of feeding a charge of brass and borax to the joint. The lower horizontal tube lug joints may be fed by ramming a piece of paper down the tube, about the centre, before fitting up; a charge can then be inserted at each end of the tube, the paper keeping them apart.

Fitting Top Back Stays.—The top back stays may now be fitted and brazed up. Before pegging up these two joints, the wheel must be tried in place, and the stays so fitted that the rim of the wheel is exactly central between them. Fit the mud-guard stay, and braze in place, to give $1\frac{1}{4}$-in. clearance between the mudguard and the tyre. The fitting and brazing of the engine lugs had better be left until the front forks are built and the engine is ready.

Fitting Front Forks.—Now the front forks may be secured. Fit and braze the steering tube to the fork crown; then square off the bottom ends of the front forks and clean out all scale, and serve the lower ends of the girder tubes in the same way. Fit the fork ends to the fork blades, set in the same manner as the rear fork ends on the front wheel, and braze up these two joints.

Next cut off the top ends of the blades to the proper length, to give the required clearance to the tyre under the fork crown. Clean the ends of the blades outside sufficiently far down to allow for the girder tube stays, then slip these stays on over the fork blades, load each with brass and borax, and fit into the crown, taking care to knock them well home. The two blades should be of exactly the same length, and, after being tested, should be fixed at an equal angle to the steering tube when the ends are the proper distance apart. Fit the wheel in the forks, and see that the rim is central between them, and use the straightedge to see that the steering tube is true with the wheel rim. When this is all assured, fix the wheel spindle or other stay between the fork ends, and peg and braze up the four joints.

The $\frac{3}{4}$-in. holes of the girder tube stays must now be cleaned out, the tubes where they fit these, and the inside of the lower ends, to fit on the front lug of the fork ends. The exact length of these two girder tubes is obtained by assembling the ball-head with balls and races in position. It is very important that the length of these shall be absolutely exact, for if they are the least bit too long, the ends would bottom in the holes of the lugs on front of the steering-tube lug before the bearing was properly adjusted. The tubes should be of such a length as to be about $\frac{3}{32}$ in. off the bottom of the holes, when the bearing is tightly adjusted. This allows for subsequent wear and adjustment of the head bearings. Of course, it is understood that the tops of these tubes are not brazed into the lugs, but are a good tight sliding fit in them. When the proper length has been obtained, take down the head and braze the four joints at the crown and lower ends. It will be as well to slip the steering tube lug on to the top ends of the girder tubes while these four joints are being brazed, thus ensuring them being the exact distance apart to drop afterwards into their places.

Before filing up the fork joints, try the front wheel again, to see if any part has sprung or given, and thus thrown the wheel out of centre. It will, of course, be better to correct this now than to wait until after the joints are filed up. While the wheel is in the fork, both before and after brazing, place the straightedge across the front of the fork crown, and see that is is parallel with the wheel spindle. Should the fork be on the twist, this can be rectified by holding the crown in the vice and inserting a bar between the lower end of the fork blades.

Handle-bar and Seat Pillar.—The handle-bar and seat pillar call for no special mention, except that they are stronger than the ordinary cycle type, and that the handle-bar is wider and longer, as already mentioned. The stem of both the seat pillar and the handle-bar should be fitted into their respective tubes before the saw-cut is made down them.

Fitting Engine Plates.—If the engine, or the crank case of the engine, is now available, the four engine plates can be fitted to the crank case. The pair on the pulley side will be let in flush with the surface of the crank case, so as to give clearance to the belt. With the engine lugs slipped on to the ends of the bottom down tube and the short $1\frac{5}{8}$-in. tube, the proper position for the $\frac{3}{4}$-in. holes in the engine plates and the correct position of the engine lugs on the tubes can be marked off to bring the engine square and perpendicular in the frame. The two lugs should be pegged on the tubes while the crank case and plates are in position with all bolts in, to ensure their coming together again properly when brazed up. It will be advisable to blacklead the inside of the $\frac{3}{4}$-in. holes in the engine lugs before brazing to prevent them scaling or getting brass on them.

Final Setting of the Frame.—The final setting of the frame should be done now. Put the bracket axle, discs, and balls together in the bracket, and, with the chain wheel and the crank fixed in position and the back wheel in the forks, line up the two chain wheels with a straightedge. With the straightedge on the outer face of the bracket wheel, the other end should just fall clear of the chain-wheel face on the back hub.

The front wheel and fork can now be fitted up in the frame, and the two wheels tested for being in track or in line. A long straightedge should be placed on the sides of the back wheel rim, and tested with the sides of the front rim. This will be done with the machine upside down. When this is set satisfactorily, place the machine right end up, and, with the straightedge on the face of the rim, see that the front fork tube is upright with the back wheel. This is done more easily if a piece of tube or a long mandrel is fitted into the steering tube.

The frame, etc., may now be filed up, and sent out to be enamelled and plated.

CHAPTER IV.

MAKING A 3½-H.P. PETROL MOTOR.

THE motor to be described in this chapter will develop 3½ h.p., and is suitable for the frame described in the previous chapters. It is quite powerful enough for use with a trailer, side, or fore car. With a two-speed gear, it may also be used for a tri-car. This is not an experimental engine, but one that has been made and well tried over some thousands of miles, giving every satisfaction. It is of original design and simply constructed with as few parts as possible (see the vertical section, Fig. 34, in which the valve springs are not shown). The patterns for all the parts are finished, and are available to readers of this handbook who would like to purchase the castings instead of making their own patterns, so that an immediate start could be made. The cylinder pattern is an exceedingly difficult one for an amateur to make; in fact, it is the work of a first-class pattern-maker to turn out a good working pattern.

Fig. 35 is a section of the cylinder through the line x x in Fig. 36, which is a plan of the top. Fig. 37 is a plan of the bottom or open end of the cylinder.

Boring Cylinder.—The first and most important part to be taken in hand is the cylinder. The boring and machining of this calls for the greatest care and skill to obtain really good results. The cylinder, etc., being all in one casting, increases the difficulty of accurate boring, but makes a much more satisfactory job when finished. Before starting the boring operation, the casting should be carefully examined for

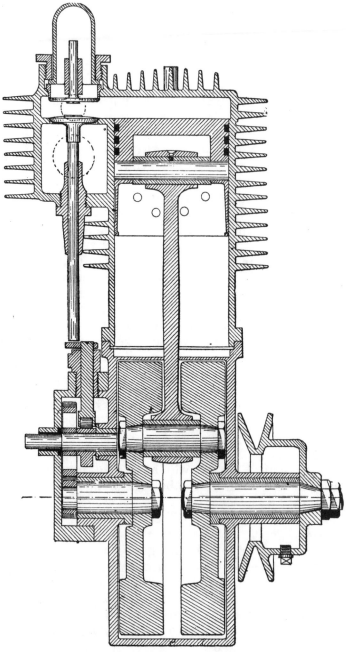

Fig. 34.—Vertical Section of 3½-h.p. Petrol Engine.

blow holes or faulty places, especially in the bore and valve seats. All sand should be thoroughly scraped out, and any rough projections filed or

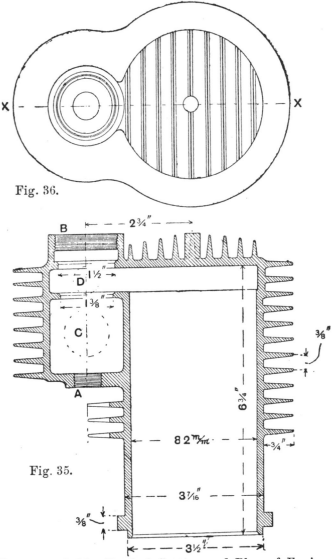

Fig. 36.

Fig. 35.

Figs. 35 and 36.—Vertical Section and Plan of Engine Cylinder.

D

carefully chipped off. The open end should be filed level, and a piece of hardwood fixed across the open end. From a centre marked on this hardwood the size of bore can be scribed off and lightly centre-dotted. The bore is 82 mm., or approximately $\frac{1}{64}$ in. under $3\frac{1}{4}$ in.; and the stroke is $3\frac{1}{4}$ in. In outlining the bore, it is advisable to mark just outside the exact bore, so that the boring will not completely obliterate the marks. There is a small boss on the top of the cylinder; this boss is perfectly central with the cylinder walls, and is placed there to assist in setting the casting true for boring, and to take the centre for turning up the outside below the radiators. The boss should be carefully centred, and drilled up with a small hole, and countersunk to the same angle as the lathe centres. Another use for this boss is to time the valves, by passing a wire down a hole drilled right through and afterwards stopped up with a small screw.

The casting may be strapped to the face plate, and bored up with a tool in the slide-rest or strapped down to the saddle and bored with a stiff boring bar held in a firm, solid chuck. By the first method, cylinders may sometimes be bored accurately, but the chances are against it. The latter method will be more satisfactory. A good stiff boring bar, not less than $1\frac{1}{2}$ in. in diameter and no longer than absolutely necessary, should be used. This should be fitted with a flat cutter made from $1\frac{1}{4}$-in. by $\frac{1}{4}$-in. steel, double cutting, the corners being rounded off and the cutting edges slightly backed off. Three cutters are required, a roughing, second, and finishing, the last being only slightly rounded on the corners and the cutting edges finely finished off on the oil-stone to the size of the bore—that is, 82 mm.

The cutter must run dead true in the lathe, or the bore will be greater than the width of the cutter. Three cuts should be sufficient, the finishing one being a mere scrape. During the finishing cut and the one before it, the lathe must not be stopped from the commencement to the finish of the cut. The job may be done with one cutter, one end only cutting, and the cutter adjusted farther out for each cut; but it should be freshly sharpened for the finishing cut. A single-ended cutter is more liable to spring and follow inequalities in the casting than a double-ended one, and for this reason at least one extra cut should be employed in the operation.

The casting must be very carefully set, and

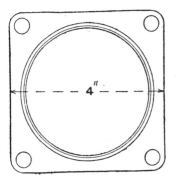

Fig. 37.—Plan of Bottom or Open End of Cylinder.

bolted down with good broad straps, one strap coming across the thick part of the valve chamber and the other across the flange at the bottom. Secured in this manner the casting is less liable to be sprung out of shape. The cylinder walls being only $\frac{5}{32}$ in. thick (finished), no allowance can be made for any inaccuracy in setting. The small lug on top of the cylinder will here be found useful, as the back centre of the lathe can be brought up close to the casting and used to test the accuracy of this end; the open end, of course, can be more easily set by the cutter edges.

The cutter slot in the boring bar should be within ¼ in. of the end, to avoid any risk of the end of the bar coming in contact with the cylinder end and thus shifting the setting; this would be disastrous in the finishing cut or the one before it. It will be noticed that the last $\frac{5}{8}$ in. of tne cylinder is shown counter-bored. It will not be necessary to bore this part if the casting is accurately set, as the casting is cored out at this part $\frac{1}{16}$ in. larger than the finished bore.

Machining Chamfer at Mouth of Cylinder.— At this setting, after the bore is finished, the chamfer at the mouth of the cylinder should be machined. This can be done with a separate cutter, or a corner of the back portion of one used for boring may be filed to the necessary shape. This chamfer is necessary for the easy insertion of the piston when the rings are in position. The extreme end may also be trued up with the cutter at this setting. This should be done to allow of the under part of the flange being $\frac{3}{16}$ in. from the end and the cylinder $6\frac{3}{4}$ in. deep. To machine the valve chamber, the casting should be firmly bolted down to a perfectly true face plate, $2\frac{3}{4}$ in. out of the centre, to get the opening true. As the surface in contact with the face plate is so small, the casting is liable to shift during machining unless it is very firmly bolted down. A sheet of brown paper placed between the face plate and the mouth of the casting will greatly assist in keeping it from shifting.

Valve Seating, Opening, etc.—When set true, bore out and screw the exhaust-valve guide holes A (Fig. 35) to $\frac{3}{4}$-in. whitworth. With a hook tool, face the under side of this hole for the collar on the guide to bed true against; this collar will be $1\frac{1}{16}$ in. in diameter. The seating for the exhaust valve will be bored out $1\frac{3}{8}$ in., the upper side being chamfered as shown and the top trued up. The opening for the inlet valve is bored out $1\frac{1}{2}$ in., and chamfered the same as the exhaust opening; $\frac{1}{4}$ in. above this bore out $1\frac{5}{8}$ in.; the remaining portion B ($\frac{3}{8}$ in.) is bored $1\frac{9}{16}$ in. bare, and screwed 20 threads to the inch, which will make it 1⅝ in. at the bottom of the thread. Face off the top of the opening true to the dimensions given.

Turning up Outside of Cylinder.—To turn up the outside of the cylinder below the radiators, the casting should be run on the centres. For this, a large centre to fit the back poppet of the lathe must be made, or the mouth of the cylinder may be bridged with a stout piece of iron or steel carefully fitted to the bore and centred true. The outside between the lower radiator and the top of the flange is turned to $3\frac{7}{16}$ in., the flange being left ⅜ in. thick, and the shoulder 3½ in. in diameter by $\frac{3}{16}$ in. deep ; this shoulder should be left with a very slight taper on it, so that it may fit tight into the opening in the top of the crank case.

Opening for Exhaust Pipe, etc.—The opening for the exhaust pipe, which is indicated by the dotted circle c (Fig. 1) in the centre of the valve chamber, must now be drilled and tapped. This is 1¼ in. by 26 threads, and is best done on the drilling machine, using a suitable tap to form the thread, as it is rather awkward to chuck or hold in the lathe. The sparking-plug hole D is drilled and tapped $\frac{23}{32}$ in. by 17 threads, and is faced on the outer surface.

Flange on Cylinder Bottom.—The flange on the cylinder bottom is left the full size at present, being filed off flush with the flange on the top of the crank case after the two parts are fitted together.

Holes for Holding-down Bolts.—The four ⅜-in. holes for the holding-down bolts, shown in the plan of the bottom end at Fig. 3, should be drilled in such a position as to leave an equal amount of metal round the corresponding holes in the crank case, but keeping the holes sufficiently far from the outer face of the cylinder to enable the corners of the bolt heads to clear properly.

Piston.—The piston casting should now be

trimmed up by filing or carefully chipping off all rough projections left from the foundry. The casting should be chucked by the projection left on the end of the casting, in a 3-jaw or 4-jaw chuck, and should not be shifted until all the turned work is finished. In setting the casting, true up from the inside, for unless the inside is true the piston will be very thin on one side when finished, as the walls will be rather light in parts. Turn up the outside perfectly parallel from end to end, 82 mm. in diameter; it should be a fairly easy fit in the cylinder at this stage. Turn as near the size as possible with a light finishing cut, and smooth off to the final fitting with a dead smooth file. True up the open end, and with a good sharp parting tool cut down the head to the projection by which the casting is held, leaving it $3\frac{1}{4}$ in. long from end to end.

Ring Grooves in Piston.—The ring grooves may now be put in; these are $\frac{3}{16}$ in. wide by $\frac{1}{8}$ in. deep, and are $\frac{1}{8}$ in. apart, the first or top one starting $\frac{1}{8}$ in. from the end. The tool with which these are cut must be carefully made and set, so as to leave the sides perfectly square and the corners sharp. A tool made as a parting tool, just $\frac{3}{16}$ in. wide, with the sides slightly backed off, will do the job at one cut, and ensure them being all the same width; but unless the lathe is a good solid tool, free from spring, the $\frac{3}{16}$-in. cut may be too much for it and set up chattering. In this case, a narrower tool must be made, not more than $\frac{1}{8}$ in. wide. Whichever way the job is done, the sides of the grooves must be perfectly parallel and square. A small sheet-metal template should be filed out for the purpose of testing them for depth and width.

Gudgeon-pin Hole.—At a distance of $1\frac{1}{4}$ in. from the top end, scribe a line round the piston with a sharp-pointed tool held in the slide-rest; on this line will be marked off the centres for drill-

ing the gudgeon-pin hole. If the lathe is provided
with a dividing plate, the centres can now be
easily marked off. Otherwise, mark the first
centre true with one of the projections on the inside of the casting ; the other centre may be
found with the dividers, or the scribing block used
on the lathe bed. It will be noticed, on reference
to Figs. 38 and 39, which are sections of the finished piston, that most of the surface between the
gudgeon-pin hole and the open end is turned down

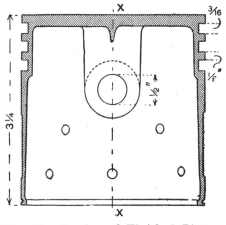

Fig. 38.—Section of Finished Piston.

a shade smaller than the main diameter. This is
done to lessen the amount of frictional surface
in contact with the cylinder walls, to lighten it,
and to help lubrication. The oil thrown up on the
inside of the piston finds its way into this recessed
part through the holes drilled therein. Another
small groove at the extreme end is cut in as shown
for a depth of $\frac{1}{32}$ in.

Inside of Piston.—The inside may now be
turned up as far as possible, leaving the walls
$\frac{3}{32}$ in. thick in the thinnest part. The inside should
taper slightly as shown, to within $\frac{1}{16}$ in. of the extreme edge, where a shoulder is left, making it

$\frac{1}{8}$ in. thick at this part. The smooth file should be
lightly run over the surface, to remove any rough
edges thrown up by the lathe tools.

Completing the Piston.—The casting can now
be parted off from the projection by which it is
held in the chuck. Care should be taken that it
does not drop off unexpectedly at the finish and
chip the thin end. The gudgeon-pin hole should
be drilled bare $\frac{1}{2}$ in. and reamered out to full $\frac{1}{2}$ in.,
with just a shade of taper ; mark the large end
with a centre-punch. The inside faces of the hole
should be trued up with a facing cutter. When
finished, they should be $2\frac{1}{4}$ in. apart, with both
faces the same distance from the outer surface.
A small special cutter bar will be required for
this job. Turn down 5 in. of $\frac{5}{8}$-in. or $\frac{9}{16}$-in. mild
steel to nicely fit the $\frac{1}{2}$-in. hole ; then, $\frac{3}{8}$ in. from
the end, cut out a slot $\frac{1}{4}$ in. by $\frac{1}{8}$ in., and fit a
cutter to suit this slot made of tool steel properly
hardened. The bar is then pushed through one
side, and the cutter tapped into position in the
bar. The cutter bar may be held in the chuck,
and the piston supported on the back centre. The
end of the cutter bar may be coned out with the
point of a $\frac{1}{2}$-in. or $\frac{5}{8}$-in. drill for a short distance if
there is any likelihood of the lathe centre meeting
the end of the bar before the cutter has done its
work. Drill about twelve $\frac{1}{8}$-in. to $\frac{3}{16}$-**in.** holes in
the recessed part as shown, and the position is
complete.

Lapping Out the Cylinder.—In the absence of
a proper lapping device, the cylinder may here be
lapped out by using the piston as a lap. Fix some
form of handle to the piston, long enough to
enable the piston to be pushed right up to the top
end of the cylinder. With some fine flour emery
and oil on the piston, work it up and down the full
length of the cylinder, frequently twisting this
also. Continue this until the piston is a very easy
fit in the cylinder—so easy that there is just the

slightest perceptible shake when the emery and oil are cleaned off. At the finish, all trace of emery must be thoroughly removed. Finish by washing out with paraffin, as there must not be the slightest trace of emery left on the cylinder or piston.

Piston Rings.—The turning and fitting of the piston rings will now be considered. There are various ways of making piston rings, but the method to be described here is as good as any, though entailing more work than some. The time occupied in turning and fitting the piston

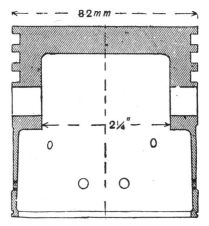

Fig. 39.—Section of Piston on Line X X (Fig. 38).

rings is time well spent; for much of the power of the engine is ensured by thoroughly well-fitting rings. Chuck the casting from which the rings are to be made by the projection on the closed end. Turn up the outside $3\frac{11}{32}$ in., and bore out the inside $3\frac{1}{16}$ in., keeping outside and inside parallel with each other. Part off, with a good sharp parting tool, four rings $\frac{3}{16}$ in. wide. They should be a rather tight fit for the grooves at this stage. The rings should not be cut in one of the two ways shown in Figs. 40 and 41. That shown in Fig. 40 is the method which the writer

greatly prefers, as, if well fitted, the joint is gas-
tight even after the usual wear causes the ring to
part slightly at the joint; and if by accident all
three ring joints get in line when working, the
gas has not a free escape, as it would have with
rings having the plain diagonal slit. The style
shown in Fig. 41, however, is the one generally
adopted, and is merely a ¼-in. diagonal cut. To
make the joint shown in Fig. 40, ¼ in. is cut
out each side for half the width of the ring, the
final fitting of the joint being done with a very

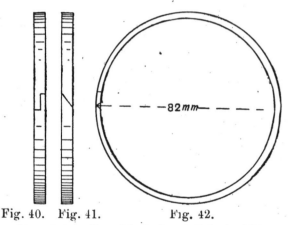

Fig. 40.   Fig. 41.   Fig. 42.

Figs. 40 and 41.—Two Methods of Jointing Piston Rings.
Fig. 42.—Piston Ring, showing Eccentricity of Bore.

fine sharp-cornered file. When the joint is
finished, two parts should fit the piston groove
as tight as possible when pressed together to
allow the parts to spring away when released.

The rings, after the joints have been made, are
sprung together in a band clip and fastened to
the face plate or a special chuck made for the
purpose; the clip is then removed, and the rings
turned and smoothed to the finished size—82 mm.
They should just enter the cylinder freely, but
without any shake, with joints tight up. Reference to Fig. 42 will show that the inner part of the

ring is eccentric with the outside; this may be obtained by setting the rings a bare $\frac{1}{32}$ in. out of truth when setting for the final turning, or when roughing out the rings the bore may be left so much smaller to allow of their being re-chucked after the outside is finished, and bored out eccentric. The thin part of the ring must come at the joint. Care must be taken not·to get the thick portion too thick, or it will not drop below the surface of the piston—which it should just do. The thick part should be a bare ⅛ in., and the piston grooves a full ⅛ in. deep, to make sure of this being correct. In fitting the rings, a file should not be used on the sides if it can possibly

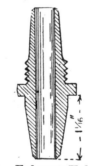

Fig. 43.—Exhaust Valve Guide.

be avoided. If the parting tool is made with the right-hand corner rather more prominent than the left corner, and the tool is kept very sharp, there will be no occasion to use the file on the sides. The rings must fit the grooves as tight as possible, without binding at any part. If the rings want easing on the sides, get a new sheet of fine emery-cloth and tack it to a perfectly level board, and rub the sides of the ring on this until a perfect fit is obtained ; use only gentle pressure and keep the ring perfectly flat.

Exhaust Valve Guide.—The exhaust valve guide, a section of which is shown at Fig. 43, is made from a piece of mild steel or from a phosphor-bronze casting. The length over all is 2½ in. ; diameter at shoulder, 1 in. ; thickness of shoulder, $\frac{3}{16}$ in. ; bore, $\frac{5}{16}$ in. Above the shoulder it is turned to ¾ in. in diameter for a distance of ⅜ in. up, and screwed ¾-in. whitworth thread. Below the shoulder, for $\frac{3}{16}$ in. down, it is turned parallel ¾ in. in diameter, or to fit the inside of the exhaust valve spring. The guide requires very careful making. The $\frac{5}{16}$-in. bore must be quite straight, and the threaded part and the top of the shoulder quite true with the bore, or the exhaust valve will not shut true on its seating. The $\frac{5}{16}$-in. hole should be bored with a twist drill or reamered out with a $\frac{5}{16}$-in. parallel rimer.

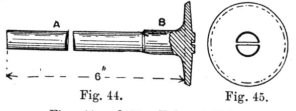

Fig. 44.   Fig. 45.

Figs. 44 and 45.—Exhaust Valve.

Three or four ⅛-in. tommy holes should be drilled in the face of the shoulder for tightening-up purposes. For turning with a spanner, this part may be made hexagon, or two flats may be filed on it. The last thread next to the shoulder should be undercut, to ensure the shoulder bedding down true on the under side of the valve chamber, which has been trued to receive it. This fitting will not require hardening.

Exhaust Valve.—The exhaust valve (Figs. 44 and 45) should be made from a single forging— that is, the forging should be made from one piece of mild steel, and should not have the head welded on to the spindle. If thought desirable, however, it may be made by screwing the end of

the stem, tapping the head to suit, and riveting
the end over into a light countersink in the head.
If made in this way, it would be an advantage
to have the head of close-grain cast-iron. The
stem A should be turned up $\frac{5}{16}$ in. a nice free fit,
without shake, in the valve guide. Finish off
with the dead smooth; and for $\frac{3}{4}$ in. to $\frac{7}{8}$ in. from
the under side of the head leave the part B full
$\frac{3}{8}$ in., as this portion of the stem is liable to get
weakened by the exhaust gases.   The head is
barely 1½ in. in diameter, and should pass freely
through the inlet valve seating in the top of the
valve chamber. Chamfer the edges to suit the

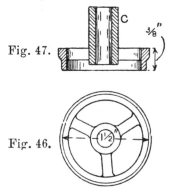

Fig. 47.

Fig. 46.

Figs. 46 and 47.—Inlet Valve Body.

angle turned on the exhaust valve seating. A
projection for grinding-in purposes is left on the
head of the valve as shown, and a saw-cut made
across it as indicated also in Fig. 45. The chamfer on the valve head must be true with the stem,
and for this reason it is advisable to turn the
whole of the valve in one position on the lathe
centres, as it is seldom that a perfectly true piece
can be produced by turning one portion in one
position and another with the piece reversed on
the centres. This proves the advantage of making
the valve from a forging, as an extension can be
left on above the head long enough for the carrier

to drive by, this being cut off after the turning is finished. The length from the under seating to the end of the stem is 6 in., and the thickness of the head at the seating is a bare $\frac{1}{8}$ in., tapering to the centre, and finished off with a good round shoulder. The valve is now finished, excepting the cotter slot or hole near the end of the stem. The exact position of this should not be determined until fitting up, as if the exhaust valve spring is purchased ready-made the position will depend on the length and strength of the spring. A slot $\frac{1}{4}$ in. by $\frac{5}{64}$ in. is best; but as this is a troublesome job, a hole may be drilled a bare $\frac{1}{8}$ in. and a round cotter used. The cotter, either flat or round, should be $\frac{3}{4}$ in. long, to fit the recess in the under part of the washer, to be described later.

Inlet Valve.—The body of the inlet valve is shown at Figs. 46 and 47. It is an iron casting, and is turned all over, excepting inside between the three arms. The casting should be chucked by the top projection, and drilled $\frac{1}{4}$ in., and then turned up to within $\frac{1}{32}$ in. of the finished size, the final turning being done on a true mandrel between the centres. The mandrel being so small in diameter, only the lightest cut is possible to avoid springing and consequent want of truth in the finished valve body. The diameter in the largest part is $1\frac{19}{32}$ in.; diameter under the chamfered portion, $1\frac{1}{2}$ in.; stem c, $\frac{11}{16}$ in. long by $\frac{1}{2}$ in. in diameter; depth without stem, $\frac{3}{8}$ in. If the inner portion between the arms requires filing out, this should be done before it is turned. The other part of the valve (Fig. 48) is made in the same way as the exhaust valve, but it is much lighter and the head is of a different pattern. The front view is similar to Fig. 45, but the diameter is only $1\frac{7}{16}$ in. The stem is $\frac{1}{4}$ in. in diameter by $1\frac{3}{4}$ in. long under the head. The head is $1\frac{7}{16}$ in. by a bare $\frac{1}{8}$ in. thick, the under side being recessed $\frac{1}{32}$ in. deep to within $\frac{1}{16}$ in. of the edge. The end of the stem is screwed twenty-four threads to the inch for ¾ in. of its length. It should be a very easy fit in the ¼-in. hole of the body, with just the least perceptible shake.

Grinding Valves.—Both valves may now be ground into their seatings with a little of the finest flour emery and oil. In grinding in, the exhaust valve, the guide (Fig. 43) must be firmly screwed up into its place in the cylinder. The body of the inlet valve must be ground into its seating in the cylinder in the same way, to make a gas-tight fit. Remove all trace of emery when finished.

Screwed Washer and Nut for Inlet Valve.— A screwed washer and nut (Figs. 49 and 50) will be required to complete this valve. The washer

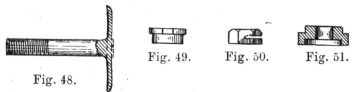

Fig. 49.   Fig. 50.   Fig. 51.

Fig. 48.

Figs. 48 to 50.—Head and Stem, Washer, and Lock-nut of Inlet Valve. Fig. 51.—Spring Washer of Exhaust Valve.

is ⅝ in. in diameter at the shoulder and ½ in. under by ¼ in. deep, and is tapped for ¼ in., twenty-four threads to the inch, to suit the screwed portion of the stem; the lower part fits inside the spring, keeping it central. The lock-nut is an ordinary hexagon ¼ in. by twenty-four threads, nut, with a saw-cut half-way through. If this nut is tightened up on to the lower washer, with the spanner gripping the upper half above the saw-cut, it will not get loose. Two flats should be filed on the shoulder of the screwed washer to hold it whilst locking the nut.

Washer for Exhaust Valve Spring.—A washer should be prepared as in Fig. 51 for the exhaust spring. This washer is $\frac{7}{8}$ in. in diameter by $\frac{1}{4}$ in. deep, with a $\frac{5}{16}$-in. plain hole to fit the stem of the exhaust valve; it is turned down on the top to fit the inside of the exhaust spring, and the under side is recessed $\frac{3}{4}$ in. in diameter to take the cotter passed through the stem. This washer serves the double purpose of holding up the exhaust spring quite central and keeping the cotter from coming out of the stem.

Valve Springs.—In making the valve springs, a certain amount of experiment with various strengths of inlet valve springs is necessary to get the best results from the engine. If too weak a spring is used, the engine may start very easily, but it will never develop its full power nor attain a high speed; while if too strong, it will be difficult to start unless a fair amount of speed is got up before dropping the exhaust lift, and the engine will run badly at slow speeds. The method of holding the spring in position with the adjustable nut and washer, as above described, will allow of a certain amount of adjustment of tension. A spring that should suit this is one made from No. 17 or No. 18 gauge wire, $1\frac{1}{8}$ in. long, with about twelve turns, and $\frac{1}{2}$ in. in diameter inside.

Valve Stems Breaking.—Trouble is sometimes experienced with this class of valve through the ends of the stems breaking off just at the end of the threaded portion, caused by the jar of the nut and washer on the top of the body at high speeds. This may be remedied by fitting a small spring inside the other one, making it a free fit on tne valve spindle. It may be made from No. 15 gauge wire with about two turns, and of such a length as to come into operation only when the valve has opened a full $\frac{1}{8}$ in. The exhaust valve spring being mechanically operated, the same degree of nicety of strength is not necessary, but it must be strong enough to shut the valve sharply

and firmly when released, otherwise there will be
loss of compression. If the spring is too strong,
there will be excessive wear and tear of the tappet rod and cam, and this may cause a fracture
of the valve just under the head.   A suitable
spring can be made from No. 14 or No. 15 gauge
wire, 2½ in. long and ¾ in. in inside diameter,
with about twenty turns.

Machining Crank Case.—Now proceed with the
machining of the crank case (see Figs. 52 to 54).
Trim up the crank-case castings, and set true, if
necessary, as it frequently happens that large,
light castings of this kind get warped or bent at

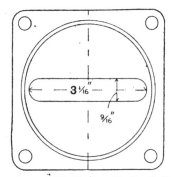

Fig. 52.—Plan of Cylinder End of Crank Case.

the foundry or in transit.   Chuck one of the castings by the central boss and turn the edge true,
and form half the joint, as shown in section at
Fig. 54.   The taper of this joint is exaggerated for
clearness ; it should have only about 1° of taper.
Face up the boss, where the shoulder of the bush
beds, and bore out the hole for the bush 1⅛ in.
The depth of the half case from the edge of the
joint to the inner face of the casting should be 1⅝
in.   The face of the boss is about ⅛ in. deep.   The
exact depth of these bosses on the inside of the
crank case should be determined after the flywheels are finished and fitted on their spindles, so
that the distance between the two bushes, when

the halves of the crank case are fitted together, is $\frac{1}{32}$ in. wider than the distance from face to face of the outer bosses of the flywheels. If it is found necessary to reduce these crank-case bosses, the casting should be tapped on to a true mandrel, run between the lathe centres for the purpose.

The other half of the crank case should be machined in the same way as the first, special care being taken to get the joint a good oil-tight fit. To insure this, turn the joint until it comes to within a bare $\frac{1}{32}$ in. of closing; then put a little powdered pumice and oil on the joint faces and grind it in to fit; this should be done while the second half is in the chuck, as the grinding-in of the joint can be finished by running the lathe with the two halves pressed lightly together. Clean off the pumice and oil, and run again for a few minutes with oil only. This done, mark the position for the half-time shaft bush A (Fig. 54), and drill the hole $\frac{11}{16}$ in. in diameter in the one half of the case. This must be done very carefully, with the centre exactly $1\frac{17}{32}$ in., from the centre of the main shaft bearing. Unless this is exact, the teeth of the gear wheels will not mesh correctly. In drilling the hole, which must be perfectly parallel with the main shaft bore, a small drill, about $\frac{1}{8}$ in., should first be run through. If the casting is placed face downwards on an upright drilling machine table, there should be no difficulty, provided the spindle is true with the table. At this time the face of the boss should be trued up with a facing cutter until the hole is $\frac{1}{2}$ in. deep. With this half of the case on a mandrel, turn off the face of the gear case until it is $\frac{13}{32}$ in. deep. The outside of the main shaft boss is also turned up true to $1\frac{15}{32}$ in. in diameter.

The two halves of the crank case are now put together, a bolt is passed through the centre holes, and screwed up with a nut and washer.

Cylinder End of Crank Case.—The case is now

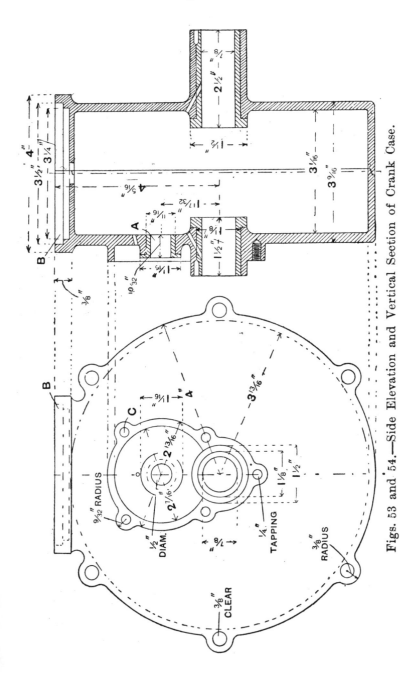

Figs. 53 and 54.—Side Elevation and Vertical Section of Crank Case.

fastened true to the face plate, and the top flange to take the cylinder (see upper part of Fig. 53, which is a plan of the gear side of the crank case) turned true; this face is $4\frac{5}{16}$ in. from the centre of the case. The recess B for the cylinder end is turned out $\frac{3}{16}$ in. deep by $3\frac{1}{2}$ in. in diameter, and should be a good tight push fit. The surface round the connecting-rod slot should be faced up true and left $3\frac{5}{16}$ in. in diameter. In setting the crank case on the face plate for this operation, it must be made absolutely true with the central hole, or the connecting-rod bearings will bind.

Bolt Holes in Crank Case.—The six $\frac{3}{8}$-in. holes shown in Fig. 52 take the bolts which hold the halves of the case together, and may now be marked off and drilled. After drilling the first hole, a $\frac{3}{8}$-in. bolt may be put through and tightened up to prevent the halves shifting during the drilling of the remaining five holes. These holes should be drilled in the lathe, halfway from each side, using a $\frac{3}{8}$-in. twist drill for the purpose, and afterwards clearing out with a parallel rimer.

Crank Case Bolts.—Four of the bolts which hold the halves together may be plain $\frac{3}{8}$-in. bright drawn steel, screwed for $\frac{3}{4}$ in. at each end to receive suitable nuts (the standard back-wheel cycle nuts may be used); these are screwed for $\frac{3}{8}$ in.— 26 threads to the inch. On account of the nuts being in the way of the belt, two of the pins will have to be made with countersunk heads, and the crank case countersunk to suit them; these two holes will be the rear top and bottom ones on the left-hand or pulley side of the engine. Small pegs should be inserted under the heads of these two pins, and suitable slots cut in the case countersink, to prevent them turning in the holes when the nuts are tightened or slackened.

The five holes c (Fig. 52) in the gear case, tapped $\frac{1}{4}$ in. whitworth, should be left until after the gear-case cover is drilled.

Hole for Oil-pipe Connection.—A hole to receive the oil-pipe connection from the pump will be necessary; this should come about halfway between the two ⅜-in. bolt holes on the front of the case in the upper half. The drilling and tapping should be left until this fitting is in hand, as the size and screwing vary.

Waste-oil Outlet.—A waste-oil outlet should be drilled and tapped ¼-in. whitworth in the extreme bottom of the case, and a screw inserted.

Air-release Valve.—An air-release valve will be fitted, and should be placed as near the centre of the gear side as possible. As the valve can be purchased for a few pence, it is not worth while to make it; a suitable size will be one screwed for ⅜ in., 26 threads to the inch.

Oil Holes in Crank Case.—Oil holes will be required, one above each of the man-shaft bearings and one just above the half-time shaft bearing (see Fig. 54). They should all have shallow V- shaped grooves cut in the side of the case leading to these oil holes; the V-grooves catch the oil running down the case sides and lead it to the holes. The one above the half-time shaft bearing is drilled right through, and is intended for oiling the gear wheels and half-time shaft. The two leading to the main-shaft bearings are drilled after the phosphor-bronze bushes have been fitted.

Attaching Cylinder to Crank Case.—The cylinder may now be fitted to the top of the crank case, and the four holes for holding the two parts together (see Fig. 53) marked off, drilled, and tapped. They are given ⅜ in. clearance in the cylinder flange, and tapped ⅜-in. whitworth in the crank case. Four studs to suit should be made for screwing permanently into the top of the crank case. Ordinary ⅜-in. set pins may be used for this purpose, but studs and nuts make a more lasting job, as the thread in the soft aluminium is liable to strip. When the four studs or pins are fitted and

screwed up, the four sides of the flanges may be
filed flush. In finally fitting the cylinder to the
crank case, a stout brown-paper washer may be
inserted between the two surfaces. It should be
noted that the recess in the top of the crank case
is slightly deeper than the length of the projection
on the bottom of the cylinder.

Gear-case Cover.—The gear-case cover, shown
in section at Fig. 55, will require turning to two
different settings inside. First chuck the casting
with the half-time shaft bearing as centre, and
turn out $2\frac{7}{16}$ in. by $\frac{7}{8}$ in. deep, facing off the edge
as far as the top lug will allow ; then shift the cast-
ing $1\frac{17}{32}$ in. out of the centre, and turn out the lower
part $1\frac{1}{2}$ in. in diameter to the same depth, and face
the edge to meet the first facing. This job requires very careful setting in the chuck to get the
facing of the edge true ; and unless this is so, and
a good level fit on the gear-case half, an oil-tight
fit cannot be obtained. The five $\frac{1}{4}$-in. holes should
then be marked off, drilled, and countersunk. The
five holes in the crank-case half of the gear case
can now be drilled and tapped, the cover being
used as a template for marking them off. The
$\frac{1}{2}$-in. hole in the cover to receive the other bronze
bush for the half-time shaft should be drilled with
a $\frac{1}{2}$-in. twist drill, after the bush has been fitted in
the crank case ; this bush having a $\frac{1}{2}$-in. hole, the
drill can be passed through that as a guide, to
insure the hole in the cover being perfectly true
with it.

While the cover is fixed to the case, the hole in
the top lug for the tappet-rod guide should be
marked off, drilled, and tapped $\frac{3}{4}$-in. whitworth.
The top of the lug should then be faced off, so
that the screwed part is $\frac{11}{16}$ in. deep. The outside
of the cover will require turning, also the projection to receive the contact-breaker bearing, the
exact size of which should be left till the contact-
breaker is purchased.

Bearing Bushes.—The bearing bushes for this motor will be hard phosphor-bronze castings, as this metal will give the best all-round results. Several good makers use hardened steel bearing bushes on their engines, and these, if thoroughly well fitted and lubricated, give good results ; but to make a success of bearings so fitted, the shafts and bushes require careful hardening and grinding, and lapping true after hardening, involving the use of special tools. One point against steel bushes

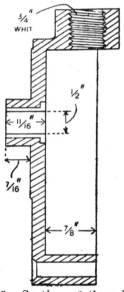

Fig. 55.—Section of Gear Cover.

is the liability of the shafts to seize or jam if lubrication fails at any time. The phosphor-bronze bushes will generally outlast the steel shafts if the metal and workmanship is good, and they have the advantage of being easier to fit. They are, however, somewhat troublesome to machine, as the tool soon loses its edge on the first cut, or if the lathe is run at too fast a speed. A slow speed will be found best—about the same as for cast-iron, or even slower, especially for the first cut, until the outer skin is removed. It will save time in tool-grinding if the castings are rough-filed all over, inside and outside, before starting to bore or turn.

Main-shaft Bushes.—The main-shaft bushes, which are shown in place in the crank case at Fig. 54 (p. 67), are bored and turned to the following dimensions: The long or pulley side bush is bored $\frac{7}{8}$ in., and turned up on a perfectly true mandrel $1\frac{1}{8}$ in. in diameter by $2\frac{1}{2}$ in. long over all, the shoulder being $1\frac{1}{2}$ in. in diameter. The bore must be absolutely parallel, and as smooth as possible. If a $\frac{7}{8}$-in. reamer is not available, the bore should be finished out with a good sharp boring tool having a flat cutting edge. But the best way is to finish the bore just a shade under $\frac{7}{8}$ in., and pass a $\frac{7}{8}$-in. reamer through the two bushes after they are in place and the two halves of the crank case bolted together; this will insure the two bearings being perfectly in line. The short bush for the gear side of the crank case is the same in bore and outside diameter as the long one, but is only $1\frac{1}{2}$ in. long. These bushes must be a good tight fit in their places, and to insure this they should be shrunk in hot. They should be turned to fit tight about halfway in—that is, the bushes should only enter their bosses in the crank case about halfway when cold. The crank case is then heated to about the heat of a good hot soldering-iron, and the bush pressed or knocked in with a mallet and cooled off at once. A small grub screw should be fitted half in the bush A (Fig. 54) and half in the crank case, to prevent the bush turning in the boss. The ends of the bushes and boss can now be faced off level on a mandrel in the lathe.

Bush for Half-time Shaft.—The bush for the large end of the half-time shaft is bored $\frac{1}{2}$ in. and turned $\frac{11}{16}$ in. by $\frac{19}{32}$ in. long, the shoulder being $1\frac{1}{16}$ in. in diameter. This should be shrunk in, in the same way as the main bushes, and secured with two small grub screws fitted through the shoulder.

Bush in Gear Cover.—The bush in the gear cover is bored $\frac{3}{8}$ in., and is $\frac{1}{2}$ in. in diameter by $\frac{11}{16}$ in. long, with the shoulder $\frac{11}{16}$ in. in diameter. It will be noticed that the shoulder of this bush is let in flush with the cover (see Fig. 55, p. 71). It is secured with a small grub screw. A small oil channel should be chipped or filed from the oil hole just above the half-time shaft in the crank case, to the edge of the bush, so that the oil may run down to the shaft and exhaust cam.

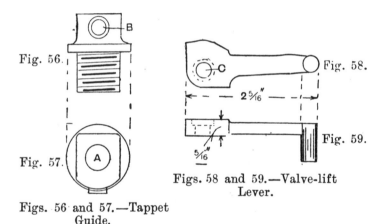

Fig. 56.

Fig. 57.

Figs. 56 and 57.—Tappet Guide.

Fig. 58.

Fig. 59.

Figs. 58 and 59.—Valve-lift Lever.

Tappet-rod Bush.—The tappet-rod bush (Figs. 56 and 57) is a phosphor-bronze casting, and is bored at A $\frac{7}{16}$ in. in diameter and turned, the bottom part, which is $\frac{11}{16}$ in. long, being screwed $\frac{3}{4}$ in. whitworth to fit tight in the tapped hole in the top of the gear cover; the shoulder at the top is turned to the same diameter as that of the lug thereon. When this bush is screwed right home, the small boss (see Fig. 57) and the hole B (Fig. 56) must come to the front; if this does not do so at the first trial, a little should be faced off the under side of the shoulder until it does. The hole B on

the front of the bush is drilled and tapped $\frac{1}{4}$-in.
whitworth, and the boss is $\frac{3}{8}$ in. in diameter by $\frac{3}{32}$
in. deep. This is to take the exhaust valve lifter
(Figs. 58 and 59), which is also a phosphor-bronze
casting. It is drilled at c $\frac{1}{4}$-in. clearance, and recessed out to fit the small boss on the tappet-rod
guide, being secured thereto with a $\frac{1}{4}$-in. screw.

Exhaust-Valve Lift.—The working of this exhaust-valve lift is as follows: The circular steel
plate riveted to the tappet rod is raised by the
upper side of the valve-lift lever, and with it the
tappet-rod and exhaust-valve stem, when the lever
is lifted by the projection on the other end. This
projection engages with a plate fixed to the lower
end of the rod which actuates the contact-breaker,
and comes into operation when the spark is retarded to its uttermost. By this arrangement one
lever does duty for the two purposes—spark advance and valve lift. This valve-lift lever is filed
and smoothed all over.

Connecting-rod Bushes.—The only other bronze
bushes to be made are the two fitted to the connecting-rod (Figs. 60 and 61), which is a mild steel
forging, machined all over. The forging should be
made by an experienced smith, and should be
forged from the solid. A drop forging made under
a steam stamp is just as good, if it can be obtained. A casting is sometimes used for this job,
either of malleable iron with bronze bushes or a
solid bronze casting. It is not advisable, however,
to use a casting in such a case for this size of
engine. The dimensions are : Length from centre
to centre, $7\frac{5}{16}$ in. ; large boss D, $1\frac{1}{4}$ in. long by $1\frac{1}{4}$
in. in diameter at the edges ; small boss E, $1\frac{1}{2}$ in.
long by 1 in. in diameter at the edges ; width and
thickness at the large boss end, 1 in. by $\frac{3}{8}$ in. ;
width and thickness at the small end, $\frac{3}{4}$ in. by
$\frac{5}{16}$ in. The bosses should be centred and drilled
$7\frac{5}{16}$ in. apart, with the holes parallel with each
other, the large end 1 in. and the small end $\frac{3}{4}$ in.

The bosses can be turned and faced on a mandrel
in the lathe. The main portion may be milled,
shaped, turned, or filed, according to what tools
are available. The bushes, which are shown in
position in Figs. 60 and 61, are 1⅝ in. long by 1 in.
outside diameter, by ¾ in. bore at the large end,
and 2⅛ in. long by 1 in. diameter by ½ in. bore at
the small end. The same instructions as regards
fitting apply as in fitting the crank-case bushes,
only that it is still more important that they

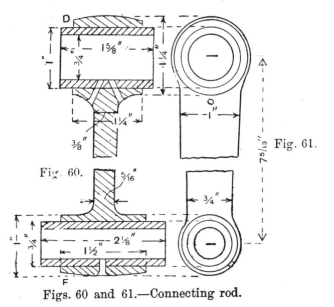

Figs. 60 and 61.—Connecting rod.

should be a good tight fit, or they will become
loose. Two ⅛-in. screws should be put through the
boss and bush to keep the bushes from turning.
The screws should be run in till the ends are level
with the bore ; the head part should then be cut
off level with the outside, and the edge of the
hole burred over to prevent the screw from coming
out. An oil hole should be drilled in the centre of
the small end and countersunk, two oil holes being
drilled in the large end, one on each side, meeting

on the inside of the bush. An oil groove should be filed along the inner surface of the bush to distribute the oil.

It is very important that the holes in the two ends of the connecting-rod should be absolutely parallel with each other in all directions, and it may therefore be necessary to set the rod to bring this about. Slip a mandrel through each end, and test this by measurement; if it requires bending or twisting, this may be done cold.

Union Nut for Induction Pipe.—The union nut for connecting the inlet or induction tube from the carburetter to the cylinder is shown in plan

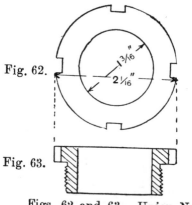

Figs. 62 and 63.—Union Nut.

and section at Figs. 62 and 63. It may be a phosphor-bronze, gunmetal, or brass casting, machined all over to the following dimensions : Bore, $1\frac{3}{16}$ in.; diameter at the screwed part, $1\frac{5}{8}$ in. by twenty threads, to fit easily the screwed opening in the valve chamber of the cylinder ; length of screwed part, $\frac{1}{2}$ in. ; diameter of collar, $2\frac{1}{16}$ in. ; depth, $\frac{1}{4}$ in. Means for tightening and slackening this out must be provided, either by filing four slots in the edge of the collar, as shown, by drilling tommy holes, or by filing the collar hexagon. By adopting the first method, the nut can always be undone on the

road by using a large nail or anything else handy
as a punch, and a spanner or stone as a hammer,
in the absence of a suitable large spanner to fit.
Flywheels.—The two flywheels may now be
taken in hand. Fig. 64 is a plan of one of them,
and Fig. 65 a section. They are $7\frac{7}{16}$ in. in outside diameter and $1\frac{1}{4}$ in. wide on the rim, and
weigh about 24 lb. the pair. If the casting is

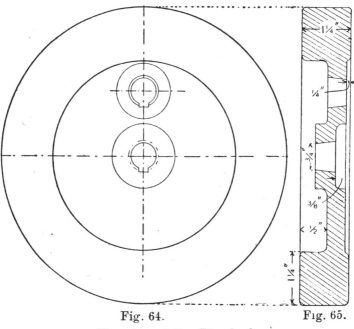

Fig. 64.   Fig. 65.

Figs. 64 and 65.—Flywheel.

chucked on the jaws of a three- or four-jaw chuck,
letting the jaws grip outward into the deep recess
under the rim, nearly the whole of one side and
edge of the rim may be machined at one operation. Turn up the rim $7\frac{7}{16}$ in. in diameter, and
true up the face of the rim and the inner edge.
Face off the centre recess $1\frac{5}{8}$ in. in diameter by
$\frac{3}{8}$ in. deep from the rim face; bore a $\frac{3}{4}$-in. hole in
the centre for the main shaft, then set the slide-

rest to 3 degrees of taper and turn out the taper
for the shaft end; this should bring the large end
of the hole to $\frac{7}{8}$ in. To make a really good and
true job of these taper holes, a reamer having a
suitable taper (3 degrees) should be used to finish
out the taper, in which case the holes should be
left from the boring tool a shade under the sizes
mentioned. The reamer should be used by bringing up the back centre as a support for the end of
the reamer, and by fixing a lathe carrier to the
reamer. A mark should be made on the face of
the reamer to insure the tool being run up to the
same depth in both holes. The job can be done
without this tool, but care must be taken to get
the rest set to exactly the same taper, and the

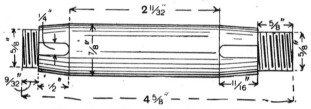

Fig. 66.—Main Shaft, Pulley Side.

tool taken to the same depth, each time. The
other flywheel may now be treated in the same
manner.

The other side of the castings has now to be
turned, but this time the casting must be held
by the outside of the rim, as the recess on this
side, under the rim, is not deep enough for the
jaws to grip. Turn up the face of the rim to
make the thickness $1\frac{1}{4}$ in.; and true the centre
part so that it is $\frac{9}{16}$ in. through from the other
face. Serve the other casting in the same way.
The casting must now be marked off for the
crank pin hole. This is 41 mm., or roughly $1\frac{5}{8}$ in.
bare. To machine this hole, fix a $\frac{3}{4}$-in. stud to the
face plate, 41 mm. out of the centre; the casting
can then be slipped over this stud by the centre

hole and brought round till the truly marked-off
centre for the crank pin is in the desired place.
Strap the casting down firmly to the face plate,
and bore a ⅝-in. hole through, and turn out to

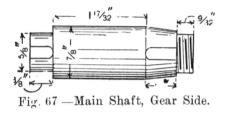

Fig. 67 —Main Shaft, Gear Side.

the same taper as the main shaft holes—namely,
3 degrees. This will bring the large side ¾ in.;
face off round this opening till it is ½ in. below
the surface of the rim face. The other side of
this hole will require facing true, for the nut to
bed against. For this operation the casting must
be reversed again on the face plate. The thickness through at this part is ½ in. full. The rim
of the flywheels may be finally trued up by mount-
ing them on their respective shafts, when these
have been turned, and running on the lathe
centres.

Main Shaft and Crank Pin.—Fig. 66 shows the
main shaft, pulley side, and Fig. 67 the gear side.

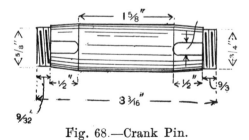

Fig. 68.—Crank Pin.

Fig. 68 is the crank pin. These may be turned
from good mild steel and case-hardened, or from
tool steel and left soft; or, if the latter steel is
used, they may be hardened and carefully tem-

pered, the centre parts being let down to a brown
and the ends right down or to a blue. In the
latter case, the hardening requires to be very
carefully done and not left too hard, or there is
a chance of fracture.

Pulley-side Main Shaft.—For the shaft (Fig.
66), cut off $4\frac{5}{8}$ in. of $\frac{15}{16}$-in. or 1-in. stuff. The dead
length finished will be $4\frac{5}{8}$ in., so that if it is cut
off on the anvil, allowance must be made for
truing up the ends. Centre the ends, and drill
up with the centre drill to the same angle as the
lathe centres. See that the rest is set to turn dead
parallel, and turn up $\frac{7}{8}$ in. from end to end, to
fit the main crank case bush nicely, without shake,
but a free fit. Turn down one end to $\frac{5}{8}$ in. for
$\frac{9}{32}$ in., and $\frac{1}{2}$ in. from this shoulder scribe a fine
line round the $\frac{7}{8}$-in. diameter, and $2\frac{11}{32}$ in. from
this scribe another line round—these are for
guides to which to turn the end of the taper part;
$\frac{11}{16}$ in. from this last line turn down $\frac{5}{8}$ in. to the
end. These $\frac{5}{8}$-in. ends require screwing twenty-
six threads per inch, to fit tightly suitable nuts,
which should be $\frac{1}{4}$ in. thick. The rest should be
set to turn the same taper as was used to bore
out the taper holes in the flywheels. Test the
shaft ends in the flywheel holes with red-lead,
until the taper end of the shaft is seen to touch
from end to end.

Short or Gear-side Main Shaft.—The short or
gear-side shaft (Fig. 67) is treated in the same
way, the plain end, to take the small gear wheel,
being $\frac{5}{8}$ in. in diameter by $\frac{3}{8}$ in. long. It is well
to leave the final size of this end until the gear
wheel is bored. The plain parallel part of this
shaft is $1\frac{17}{32}$ in., the taper part $\frac{1}{2}$ in., and the
screwed part $\frac{9}{32}$ in. The crank pin (Fig. 68) is
turned from a piece of $\frac{13}{16}$-in. or $\frac{7}{8}$-in. stuff; the
diameter is $\frac{3}{4}$ in., to fit the large end of the connecting-rod bush, and it is $3\frac{3}{16}$ in. long over all.
The two ends are $\frac{5}{8}$ in. by $\frac{9}{32}$ in., screwed twenty-

six threads per inch; the taper parts are ½ in.
long, and the parallel parts 1⅝ in. The taper
parts of all three shafts must be a perfect fit in
their respective holes in the flywheels, and care
must be taken that the shoulders at the end of
the threaded parts do not come right through the
holes in the flywheels. When the shafts are right
home, and the nuts screwed up hard, the face
of the nuts should bed against the flywheel before
it touches the shoulder on the shaft end by about
$\frac{1}{32}$ in. Should the nut face touch the shaft shoulder before it beds against the flywheel, it will
not be long before the flywheels are loose on their
shafts and out of truth. In making these three
shafts it will, of course, be best and quickest to

Fig. 69.—Half-time Shaft.   Fig. 70.—Tappet Rod.

turn all the taper parts at one setting of the
rest, and also to do all the screwing at one time.
   Half-time Shaft.—The half-time shaft (Fig.
69) may as well be made at this stage, though the
large gear wheel and exhaust cam should be
finished first, so as to be able to get the shaft a
good tight fit. The finished size is 2⅝ in. over all.
The main part is ½ in. in diameter by 1⅝ in. long,
to fit tightly the bore of the gear wheel and exhaust cam. The ⅜-in. part is 1 in. long, to fit the
bush in the gear cover of the crank case freely.
   Tappet Rod.—The tappet rod (Fig. 70) is
turned from a piece of tool steel, and need only
be hardened on the extreme end (the round end).
It is $\frac{7}{16}$ in. in diameter, with the end nicely
rounded and smoothed off. The top end is turned
down to ⅜ in. for ¼ in., to take the circular plate
(Fig. 71), which should be a piece of mild steel

$\frac{3}{16}$ in. thick by $1\frac{1}{8}$ in. in diameter, case-hardened, and firmly riveted on the tappet rod. This rod should fit the tappet guide (Figs. 56 and 57, p. 73) without shake.

Gudgeon Pin.—The gudgeon pin (Fig. 72) may be a piece of tool steel $3\frac{5}{32}$ in. long by $\frac{1}{2}$ in. in diameter. It is turned to fit the piston tightly, the piston having been reamered out slightly taper; and the pin must have a corresponding amount of taper. It should be a light driving fit, so that the small end does not come quite flush with the outside of the piston by about $\frac{1}{32}$ in.

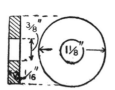

Fig. 71.—Circular Plate of Tappet Rod.

Fig. 72.—Gudgeon Pin.

The large end is then covered with a brass washer $\frac{1}{2}$ in. in diameter, which will prevent the pin working back and scoring the cylinder walls. This method of fixing the gudgeon pin, though simple, has been found to be very effective; but it is most important that it should be a good tight fit in the piston, and fitted with a slight degree of taper. Set pins, however well fitted and secured by split pins, etc., are never reliable.

It will probably be found, upon trying the gudgeon pin in the connecting-rod bush, that it is too tight a fit. If so, the bush should be reamered out until the pin is a good fit without

shake. A piece of brown paper on one side of
the reamer will cause it to cut a shade larger than
if used without. The pin should be hardened,
and let down to brown in the centre and blue
at the ends. In hardening, do not get the steel
so hot as to scale, or the fit will be upset, and dip
quite straight in the water end on. In fitting the
gudgeon pin to the piston, be sure that both ends
are equally tight in the piston holes, or it will
soon work loose. Do not harden the shafts until
the keyways have been cut and the crank case
with the flywheels have been fitted together and
assembled.

Cutting Keyways in Shafts.—A simple and at
the same time thoroughly efficient method of cutting the keyways in the various shafts will now be

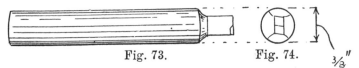

Fig. 73.   Fig. 74.   ⅓″

Figs. 73 and 74.—Tool for Cutting Keyways in Lathe.

given. All that has to be made, for cutting keyways in an ordinary slide-rest lathe, is the tool
shown at Figs. 73 and 74. It is turned from a
piece of ⅜-in. or ½-in. tool steel, the end being
reduced to a diameter corresponding to the width
of the keyway to be cut. This portion of the tool,
for the present purpose, will be ¼ in. in diameter
by ⅜ in. long; it is as well to keep this part short,
to prevent springing of the tool as far as possible.
The reduced part is then filed on each side until it
is $\frac{3}{32}$ in. thick; the sides are backed off slightly,
and the two cutting edges filed as shown. The
end is then hardened in the usual way, and let
down to a dark straw colour at the cutting edges.
The tool is next mounted in the lathe chuck to run
true, and the shaft to be cut is clamped in the
tool-holder of the slide-rest, at right angles to the

tool, and with its axis perfectly level with the lathe centres. The shaft is fed up to the cutter by means of the slide-rest, a start being made at the inner or rounded end of the keyway; the top slide is then worked for the required length of the keyway. Not more than $\frac{1}{32}$ in. in depth should be taken at one cut, or the tool may break. Provided the shaft is set true in all directions in the tool post, and the cutter is sharp, a perfect keyway is the result, equal in every respect to one cut in a keyway or slotting machine. The various keys may be fitted by filing flats on the shafts for the keys, but this method, unless the fitting is very well done, is not recommended. The simple method described above will be found much more reliable, and, of course, is quicker once the tool has been made. Besides which, the tool will cut other keyways of the same width.

All the keyways in the two main shafts, crank pin, and half-time shaft are of the same width and depth, that is, $\frac{1}{4}$ in. by $\frac{1}{8}$ in. The length of the keyway in the half-time shaft is 1 in.; the others are cut as long as possible. The keyways in the flywheels, gear wheel, and exhaust cam should be filed, if a slotting machine is not available; they must be quite flat and straight, with no taper. In fitting the keys, which should be made from cast steel, file on the sides first, to fit the width of the keyways; then true up one face perfectly flat, and fit the key carefully in its place by filing on the other face only. Do not cut off the key until it has been perfectly fitted, and this is not attained until the key beds on its seating from end to end on both sides. The fitting of all keys on a motor of this kind calls for special care, as a wheel fitted to a shaft with anything but first-class workmanship is sure to work loose sooner or later.

Engine Belt Pulley.—Fig. 75 is a section of the engine belt pulley, which is an iron casting. The pattern should be made in two parts, parting at,

the bottom of the belt groove. A core box is not
absolutely necessary, as the inside can be left
parallel and the recessed portion turned out of
the casting. This recessed part is for retaining
any oil which may work out of the crank case
through the main bearing, and prevent it being

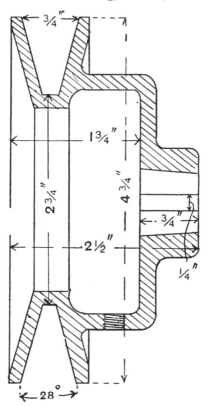

Fig. 75.—Section of Engine Pulley.

thrown over the outside of the engine. A drain-
hole is drilled, tapped, and fitted with a ¼-in.
Whitworth screw. If this screw is removed from
time to time, and any oil which has accumulated
drained off, this side of the engine at any rate will
be kept free from oil. Chuck the casting in the
·jaw chuck, large side outwards ; bore a ¾-in. hole,

and turn out 3 degrees taper, to suit the taper of the main shaft. Turn up the outer edge of the rim $4\frac{3}{4}$ in. in diameter; and turn out the belt groove 28 degrees, $\frac{3}{4}$ in. wide at the top. The bottom of the belt groove is $2\frac{3}{4}$ in. in diameter. Clear up the inside, and turn out the recessed part. The back should be $1\frac{3}{4}$ in. from the face. The face of the boss for the lock-nut to bed against may be trued up with a hook tool at this setting, the length of the boss for the shaft being $\frac{3}{4}$ in. through.

The casting may now be mounted on its shaft, and the remainder of the outside turned up on the lathe centres. This pulley is designed for a $\frac{3}{4}$-in. belt, which is strong enough if the engine is to be

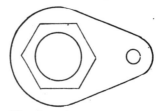

Fig. 76.—Locking Plate.

used for a single cycle; but if for use with a trailer, $\frac{7}{8}$ in. is advisable, while for tri-car work a 1-in. belt is required. For the 1-in. belt the casting must be $\frac{1}{8}$ in. to $\frac{3}{16}$ in. wider at the belt groove, but the present casting will turn out for the $\frac{7}{8}$-in. size. A keyway $\frac{1}{4}$ in. wide by $\frac{1}{8}$ in. deep must be cut the length of the bore.

Securing Pulley to Shaft.—This pulley is secured on its shaft by two $\frac{1}{4}$-in. thick lock-nuts, screwed to fit the $\frac{5}{8}$-in. by 26 threads at the shaft end, besides the key. An alternative method of fixing the engine pulley to the shaft is to screw the end of the shaft with a right-hand thread, $\frac{3}{4}$ in. by 26 threads, and the pulley bore to suit, in place of the plain taper and key, and fit a left-hand thread lock-nut, $\frac{5}{8}$ in. by 26 threads to the inch. This

makes a reliable fixing, but the pulley is sometimes very difficult to remove if it gets jammed on
the thread.

Pinning Lock-nut to Shaft.—The lock-nuts
which secure the two main shaft ends to the flywheel, and one end of the crank pin, may be
secured permanently by drilling a ⅛-in. hole half in
the nut and half in the end of the shaft, and then
driving in a pin which is $\frac{1}{16}$ in. shorter than the
hole is deep, and burring the edge of the hole over
the pin. The drilling must be done before the
shafts are hardened, the pinning being the last
operation of all when finally assembling.

Safety Lock for Crank Pin Lock-nut.—The
lock-nut on the other end of the crank pin will re-

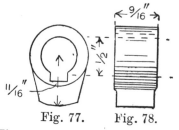

Fig. 77.　Fig. 78.

Figs. 77 and 78.—Exhaust Cam.

quire a safety lock, but it should be of such a
nature that will allow of removal for future repairs, etc. Such a lock may be made by fitting
a sheet-steel plate cut out of No. 15 or No. 16
gauge sheet, as shown at Fig. 76. This is slipped
on over the lock-nut after it has been tightened
right up, and the small end secured to the face of
the flywheel with a small screw tapped into the
flywheel, which must be a good tight fit on the
thread, and have a good strong head.

Exhaust Cam.—The exhaust cam (Figs. 77 and
78) is made from tool steel carefully hardened and
tempered. The dimensions are—bore, ½ in., to fit
tight on the half-time shaft; diameter, $1\frac{1}{16}$ in.,

with a ¼-in. lift ; it is ₁⁹₆ in. wide, and keywayed ¼ in. by ⅛ in. Harden right out, polish, and let down to a brown on the wearing surface, and get the inside as low as possible ; this may be done by making an iron rod very hot and inserting it in the hole, letting the hot rod bear most on the thick side of the cam, or the thin side will be let down too low before the thick or lift side is low enough.

Gear Wheels.—Plans and sections of the large and small gear wheels are shown at Figs. 79 to 82 ; these actuate the exhaust and ignition cams on the half-time shaft. The large gear wheel may be

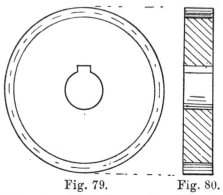

Fig. 79.   Fig. 80.
Figs. 79 and 80.—Large Gear Wheel.

in phosphor-bronze, and has 32 teeth ; it is 2 in. in diameter on the pitch line, 2⅛ in. in diameter over all, has a ½-in. hole to fit tight the half-time shaft, and is ⅜ in. thick on the face of the teeth. The small gear wheel is of good tough, mild steel, case-hardened. It has 16 teeth, is 1 in. in diameter on the pitch line, 1⅛ in. in diameter over all, has a ⅝-in. hole to fit tight the end of the main shaft, and is ⅜ in. wide on the face of the teeth. It should be keywayed only ₁¹₆ in. deep by ¼ in. wide. If the keyway is cut any deeper than this, the wheel will not be strong enough, and will be liable to burst when the key is fitted up. In the absence of proper facilities for gear-cutting, this part of

the work must be put out to be done. The blanks
can be bored and turned to the sizes given, and
sent to a firm who make a speciality of this class
of work ; or they may be purchased finished from
most dealers in motor parts. If the cutting is
done at home, two cutters will be required, one
for the driven wheel and one for the driver, the
shape of tooth being different in each. If wheels
of exactly the same number of teeth cannot be
purchased, they may have 30 and 15 or 28 and 14,
so long as they are the same diameter on the pitch
line. It is not advisable to have finer teeth than
would be in wheels of 32 and 16, of these pitch

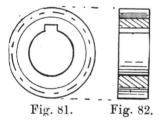

Fig. 81.   Fig. 82.
Figs. 81 and 82.—Small Gear Wheel.

diameters, as they would be weaker ; and coarser
than 28, and 14 would be too large for the purpose.
In fitting up the large gear wheel and exhaust
cam to the half-time shaft, the gear wheel is fitted
with one face level with the shoulder at the finish
of the ⅜-in. part, and the exhaust cam behind it.

Cutting Keyway in Large Gear Wheel.—Cutting the keyway in the large gear wheel should
be left until the parts are assembled, as the timing
of the exhaust valve lift and closing can be set
to a nicety by shifting this wheel a trifle on its
shaft. It will here be found advantageous to
have the wheel a good tight fit on the shaft, as
the friction will keep the wheel in position whilst
the timing is done. The position of the keyway
can then be marked accurately whilst in place.

Induction or Inlet Pipe.—The induction or

inlet pipe from the engine to the carburettor is illustrated at Fig. 83. This is made from 1½-in. No. 16 gauge weldless steel tube bent to the shape shown. About 10 in. is actually taken up in the bend illustrated, but a length of at least 1 ft. 4 in. or 1 ft. 6 in. will be required for the purpose, as the bends finish so near the ends. The tube should be rammed as tight as possible with fine dry sand, and the ends stopped with metal plugs. The tube is heated 2 in. or 3 in. at a time to a good bright heat, and bent to a radius of 1¾ in. The two ends should be quite parallel with each other, or the carburettor will not be upright when fitted to the engine. A steel washer or collar, turned all over, is brazed to one end, the union nut holding the pipe securely to the engine by this collar. The other end of the pipe will be fitted with a suitable union to fit the carburettor connection. The type of this connection will depend upon the size and pattern of carburettor used. A suitable carburettor for the engine will be a Longuemare, Model H, or the device described in the next chapter. It will be 'advisable to purchase this fitting instead of attempting to make it, unless the worker is very skilful.

Contact-breaker.—The type of contact-breaker to be used has now to be chosen. This may be of the wipe type with a trembler coil, or a make-and-break with a plain coil. Opinions are divided as to which is preferable for a motor cycle ignition. With a wipe contact and trembler coil easy starting is facilitated, and risk of miss-fires is lessened, but the engine will not attain the high rate of speed that it will with a make-and-break and a plain coil. Neither can the timing be set to the same degree of nicety as with the make-and-break. Against the latter system there is frequent trimming up and adjustment of platinum contact points, and sometimes difficulty in starting, unless these two items are perfect. For ordinary purposes, the wipe contact and trembler coil are preferable. Whichever system is adopted, the contact-breaker will be purchased ready-made with ignition cam, or wipe sector. This cam or sector will be fitted on the small end of the half-time shaft.

Assembling the Engine.—With all the component parts made and finished, the final assembling of the engine may now be started. The two main shafts should be fitted to their respective flywheels, the nuts screwed right home, and secured with small pegs in the nuts and shaft ends. One half (the gear-side half for preference) of the crank

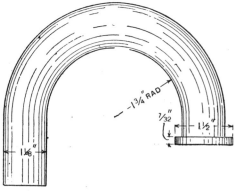

Fig. 83.—Inlet Tube from Carburettor.

pin should be served in a similar manner. The rings should be fitted to the piston grooves, and the piston to the connecting-rod by the gudgeon pin, which must be tapped in far enough to allow of the ½-in. brass covering washer clearing the cylinder walls when the piston is in, but not so far that the opposite end will touch the opposite side of the cylinder.

The connecting-rod may now be slipped over the crank pin, and the flywheels fitted together by the other end of the crank pin; the nut is then tightened, and the flywheels tested between the

lathe centres for truth. If out of truth, some part
has been put together improperly, or one of the
taper ends of the shafts may have some grit or
dirt on it, thus preventing a true fitting of the
surfaces. If true, lock the nut as tight as it will
go, and fit on the sheet-steel locking device (Fig.
76, p. 86).

Balancing the Flywheels.—It will be found that
the balance weights cast on the flywheels are not
sufficient to balance the weight of the crank pin,
connecting-rod, and about half the weight of the
piston; therefore ⅝-in. holes should be drilled in
the rim of the flywheels, on the crank pin side,
to balance this. A weight equal to the above-mentioned fittings may be suspended from the crank,
whilst flywheels are lightly held between the centres of the lathe. If sufficient metal cannot be
taken out of the rims in this manner, without
unduly weakening them, holes can be drilled in
the opposite side of the rims (balance-weight
side), and filled with lead. To prevent any
possibility of this lead working loose, drill the
holes through the side of the rim, and then
drill other holes from the outer edge to meet the
first; this will form T-shaped openings, into
which the lead may be cast without fear of its
coming out. Fit the two halves of the crank case
together, with the flywheels in place.

Bolting up Crank Case.—The air valve, oil
connection, and drain plug all being fitted, see
that the edges of the case are quite clean and
coated with red-lead and oil. Bring the halves
together. Insert two of the ⅜-in. bolts, which hold
the halves together, at opposite points, screw up,
and test the flywheels for freedom of running before proceeding further. If satisfactory, insert
the rest of the ⅜-in. bolts and screw up.

Fitting Cylinder to Crank Case.—The cylinder
can now be fitted on to the crank case. See that
the surfaces that come together are perfectly clean.

Cut out a stout brown-paper washer to go between the cylinder flange and the top of the crank case. Bolt down equally, and test for free working; by fastening a lathe carrier on to the end of the shaft, the flywheels can be revolved. If this does not work so free as it should, making due allowance for friction of the piston rings, etc., remove and find out the cause.

Completing the Assembling.—It should be mentioned that all parts are to be oiled, as they go together; and in fitting piston rings, see that the joints are equally divided. Key on the 16-tooth wheel to the end of the main shaft when everything works free. The tappet-rod guide should be screwed up tight in the gear-cover top, and the half-time shaft tried in its place with the gear cover on. Key on the exhaust valve cam to its shaft, tap on the large gear wheel temporarily, fit up the exhaust valve, put the gear cover on, and slip in the tappet rod. The end of the exhaust-valve stem should come within $\frac{1}{32}$ in. of the plate on the tappet rod, when the valve is right down on its seating and the cam is out of operation. When this has been so arranged, harden the end stem of the valve.

Timing the Engine.—The timing is a very important operation, and may now be attended to. Get a piece of stout wire that will pass through the small hole drilled in the top of the cylinder, and on this wire make a mark level with the top of the cylinder when the piston is at its highest point in the cylinder, the end of the wire resting on the top of the piston. Turn the main shaft (by the carrier) until the piston has descended to its lowest point, then make another mark on the wire in the same way as before. It is now possible to tell to a nicety when the piston is at its highest and lowest point in the cylinder. Now so arrange the large gear wheel on the half-time shaft that the cam will cause the exhaust valve

just to start opening when the piston has descended four-fifths of its stroke in the cylinder,
and the valve shuts dead on its seating upon the
completion of the next up stroke. The meshing
of the gear wheel teeth must be altered until the
desired effect is obtained, when the exact position
for the keyway on the large wheel can be marked
and cut and keyed up. It may be necessary to
alter the shape of the cam slightly (by grinding,
if it has been already hardened) to bring about
the desired effect.

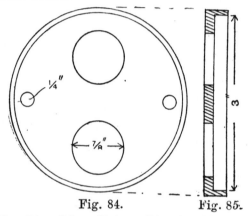

Fig. 84.   Fig. 85.

Figs. 84 and 85.—Bottom Plate of Silencer.

Timing the Ignition.—The timing of the ignition is the next operation. The ignition cam
must be fixed to the end of the half-time shaft
in such a position that the spark will pass when
the piston is at the top of its compression stroke,
with the contact-breaker case or rocker in its midway position. This will allow for retarding and
advancing the spark to the desired amount. It
must be noted that the actions of a wipe contact
and a make-and-break are different in this respect
—that whereas with the wipe the spark will pass
at the plug points immediately the brass section
of the fibre cam touches the block on the spring
wiper, with the make-and-break the spark does

not pass when the platinum points are brought together by the action of the ignition cam, but at the break—that is, immediately the cam allows the points to spring apart. Due allowance for this must therefore be made when fitting up either of these systems. It only remains to fit in the inlet valve, fit on the belt pulley, and fill in the small hole in the cylinder head with its screw, and the engine is complete, less the silencer.

Silencer.—A simple but thoroughly effective silencer has been designed for this engine, the

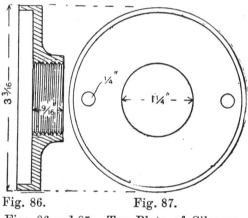

Fig. 86.   Fig. 87.

Figs. 86 and 87.—Top Plate of Silencer.

component parts being shown at Figs. 84 to 89. The outside cylinder is not shown, as it needs no illustration to make it clear. It is simply a plain sheet-iron cylinder, 10 in. by 3 in., outside measurement, and about No. 18 gauge. It can be joined as stove piping is joined, by simply lapping the edges over each other and hammering flat on a mandrel, or the edges may overlap ½ in. and be riveted together with small iron rivets. Figs. 84 and 85 show the bottom end, and Figs. 86 and 87 the top. These are malleable iron castings, turned to the dimensions given. The top flange is screwed for 1¼ in., 26 threads to the inch,

and drilled with two $\frac{1}{4}$-in. holes, $1\frac{3}{16}$ in. from the
centre. The bottom flange is drilled with two $\frac{7}{8}$-in.
holes $\frac{3}{4}$ in. from the centre, and two $\frac{1}{4}$-in. holes to
correspond with those in the top flange. They
are turned to fit tight over the 10-in. by 3-in.

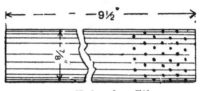

Fig. 88.—Tube for Silencer.

cylinder.   Two $\frac{7}{8}$-in. by No. 16 gauge weldless
tubes, $9\frac{1}{2}$ in. long, are stopped at one end by having two washers brazed in, and seven rows of
$\frac{1}{16}$-in. holes (about eighteen to the row) are drilled
in the stopped ends (see Fig. 88).   The open ends
of these tubes are knocked tight into the $\frac{7}{8}$-in.
holes in the bottom flange and brazed.   The whole
is held together by the two $\frac{1}{4}$-in. pins (Fig. 89),
which are $10\frac{3}{4}$ in. long and screwed at the ends
$\frac{1}{4}$-in. Whitworth, and fitted with a nut at each
end. The nuts must be a good tight fit on the
thread—in fact two of them can be riveted over.

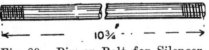

Fig. 89.—Pin or Bolt for Silencer.

Exhaust Pipe.—The exhaust tube to connect
the silencer to the engine will be of weldless tube,
$1\frac{1}{4}$ in. by No. 16 gauge screwed to suit.   The length
and shape will depend upon the position in which
the silencer is fixed.

CHAPTER V.

SPRAY CARBURETTOR FOR 3½-H.P. MOTOR.

MOST readers of this book will be familiar with the function of a carburettor, and will know that originally the carburettor was of the surface type —that is, the air on its way to the engine cylinder was carburetted (saturated with petrol vapour) by being obliged to bubble up through petrol contained in a suitable vessel. For years, now, the spray carburettor has been in general use, although quite occasionally the surface carburettor can still be found doing good work.

A carburettor is, in simple words, a gas-maker. The carburettor's air intake pipe often has a bell-mouth so as to collect, as it were, the air from the surface of the motor head and cylinder. The air being so warmed assists the action of the carburettor in cold weather, or when petrol of greater than ordinary density is being used. It will be understood that the air is sucked into the carburettor on the first outward stroke of the piston in the engine's four-stroke-cycle. As the air rushes up past a nozzle, which is in connection with the petrol supply, a thin stream of petrol is caused to be ejected from the nozzle into the vaporising chamber. In many designs of carburettor, the stream of petrol impinges on a cone or mushroom, which assists in breaking up mechanically the drops of petrol. The air in motion has a great capacity for absorbing the petrol particles, and as it passes onward to the cylinder, the peculiar mechanical construction of the upper part of the carburettor, and possibly the heat of the various parts, assist in making the mixture of air and petrol still more intimate, until when the mixture reaches the engine cylinder it may be regarded, for the moment only, as a true gas. The ignition and the consequent expansion of the combustible gas in the engine cylinder provides the working stroke, which gives impulse to the crankshaft and flywheel.

It is usual to provide a carburettor with what is known as a float-feed, this being a simple device by means of which the ingress of the petrol from the petrol tank is regulated by a float, which opens or closes the petrol inlet valve according to the quantity of petrol in the float chamber, between which and the spraying nozzle alluded to above there is a tubular connection. This float device prevents flooding of the carburettor, but most carburettors have projecting from them a small rod, by means of which the action of the float can be momentarily suspended for convenience in obtaining a rich mixture when starting the engine.

The simple carburettor illustrated and described in this chapter has been in use for some two or three years, and has proved very efficient. It has been used on engines of from 2 h.p. to $3\frac{1}{2}$ h.p., and works equally well with any engine within this range, and would no doubt be quite suitable for one of 4 h.p. to $4\frac{1}{2}$ h.p. by adjusting the petrol tap to pass more petrol. Fig. 90 is a full-size sectional view of the complete carburettor and throttle valve. All the illustrations in this chapter are reproduced full size.

The whole of the castings are brass, the needle valve A is of steel, and the cone piece B of fine copper gauze.

The top part, which contains the throttle valve, can first be taken in hand. The casting is chucked by the small end, and bored right through $\frac{7}{8}$ in. diameter, the large end being bored out 2 in. by $\frac{1}{4}$ in. deep and tapped internally with any

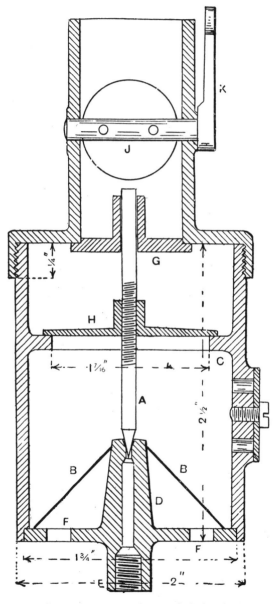

Fig. 90.—Sectional View of Carburettor.

convenient fine thread for screwing to the main
body piece. Or, instead, the two parts can be
connected by a plain push-on fit, and secured by

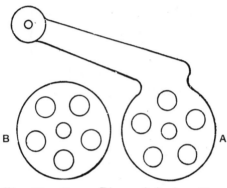

Fig. 91.—Cover Piece of Carburettor.

putting three or four small screws through the
flange of the top piece into the main body piece.

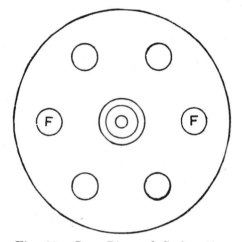

Fig. 92.—Base Piece of Carburettor.

This method will answer very well if screwing
is inconvenient, but it must be a good tight fit.
The main body piece is now chucked by the top

end, and the bottom edge faced off and recessed out 1⅞ in. diameter by ⅛ in. deep, to receive the bottom or base piece. The casting is then reversed in the chuck, and the top edge faced and the outside turned to fit the top piece and screwed if necessary. The internal flange c is bored out 1$\frac{7}{16}$ in. diameter and faced on the top side only.

The extra air holes should now be drilled in the side of the body piece. These are five $\frac{3}{16}$-in. holes spaced equally distant on a ⅝-in. circle, the

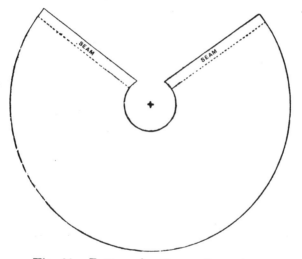

Fig. 93.—Pattern for Gauge Cone-piece.

centre being drilled and tapped to receive a small cheesehead screw by which the cover piece (Fig. 91) is held in position. This piece requires drilling the same, so that the holes in the body can be completely covered or fully open. The face of this extra inlet and also the cover piece (Fig. 91) must be trued up so that one fits flat against the other.

The base piece D (Fig. 90), and shown separately by Fig. 92, is now drilled in the centre ¼ in. diameter, or to suit the thread of the small petrol tap to be fitted here, for ⅜ in. up. Then a ⅛-in. hole is drilled to within ¼ in. of the top, this last $\frac{1}{4}$ in. being drilled right through $\frac{1}{16}$ in. diameter with the top end coned out as shown to take the bottom end of the needle valve. This piece should now be mounted between the lathe centres and turned all over, $1\frac{7}{8}$ in. diameter by a bare $\frac{1}{8}$ in. thick, to fit tightly the recess in the body pieces, to which this base piece is finally fixed by riveting, or by spinning over the thin edge of the bottom of the body.

The bottom piece E (Fig. 90) is turned $\frac{3}{8}$ in. diameter by $\frac{3}{8}$ in. long, and the top conical part D is turned $\frac{7}{8}$ in. long by $\frac{3}{8}$ in. at the base, tapering to $\frac{9}{32}$ in. at the top. The air holes F (Figs. 90 and 92) are six in number, $\frac{7}{32}$ in. in diameter, equally spaced on a $1\frac{1}{4}$-in. circle. The gauze cone piece B (Fig. 90) should now be cut out, bent

Fig. 94.—Bridge Piece of Carburettor.

to shape, and soldered at the joint and to the base piece D at the top and all round at the bottom, so that the petrol issuing from the top of the small hole flows over the copper gauze cone. Fig. 93 shows the size and shape for cutting out this piece.

The bridge piece G (Fig. 90, see also Fig. 94) should now be drilled $\frac{1}{8}$ in., and the shoulders turned true with the hole. The piece is then soldered in position as shown.

The valve piece H (Fig. 90) is now drilled $\frac{1}{8}$ in. tapping size, and turned up true with the hole, $1\frac{5}{8}$ in. diameter by $\frac{3}{32}$ in. thick at the centre part, tapering to a bare $\frac{1}{16}$ in. at the edges; the boss on the top is $\frac{5}{16}$ in. in diameter by $\frac{5}{16}$ in. long. It should be tapped and screwed to the needle valve A, which is a piece of $\frac{1}{8}$-in. steel wire, straight and true.

After the valve piece H is screwed to the needle-valve piece and locked by a small lock nut (not shown), it should be mounted between the lathe centres and the brass piece H skimmed up true. The point can be turned quite at the last, before parting off the centre on which it was turned. The brass piece H is fixed in such a position on the needle valve that the point shuts dead on the hole at the same time as the under edge of the piece H just touches the flange of the body piece. These two joints may finally be ground in with just a touch of powdered pumice powder and oil, or crocus powder.

A loose distance piece is slipped on the stem of the needle valve just above the boss of H, to prevent the valve opening more than ⅛ in., and a light helical spring is made to fit over the boss of H and bear against the under side of the bridge piece G. This spring must be light, and rather weaker than the inlet-valve spring of the motor.

The throttle valve is a disc of brass about No. 18 gauge riveted or screwed to the casting J, which is $\frac{3}{16}$ in. in diameter, with half filed away where the disc fits. The operating level is one with the piece to which the disc is fastened.

The petrol regulating tap to screw into the bottom of E can be purchased for 9d. to 1s., and should be of about 2½ mm. bore.

The outside of the body can be polished and plated to give a good finish.

CHAPTER VI.

IGNITION COILS FOR MOTOR CYCLES.

WHEN petrol is vaporised, and its vapour combined with air, it forms an explosive mixture which may be used as a propulsive force in driving a motor. It is thus utilised in specially constructed engines, resembling gas engines, the construction of which has been fully described in the previous chapters. The explosive mixture of petrol vapour and air is admitted into the cylinder of the motor, and exploded there by means of electric sparks from an inductor coil specially constructed for the purpose, and called an ignition coil. This is worked with electric current obtained from a primary battery, or from a 4-volt accumulator, the latter being preferred because of its superior constancy to that of a primary battery.

Ignition coils for petrol motors may be made in one or two types : (1) a plain primary coil with a wipe arrangement to cause the spark, and (2) a compound primary and secondary coil with a trembler break and a wipe arrangement combined to produce the spark.

To make a plain or primary coil, first procure enough No. 22 gauge iron wire to form a bundle 12 in. long and ¾ in. in diameter, for the core of the coil. Cut a number of 12-in. lengths, and pack as many as possible into two ¾-in. curtain rings. Then carefully push some lengths down the centre of the bundle until it fits the rings tightly. Next bind the bundle tight with soft iron wire, put in a dying forge or kitchen fire, heat to a red heat, and allow to cool down as the fire dies out during a period of several hours. This anneals the iron and makes it quite soft, a necessary property in the core of a coil to ensure rapid magnetisation and de-magnetisation.

If hard iron is employed in making a core, more electricity is required to magnetise the iron, and it retains the magnetism after the electric current is shut off, whilst a similar result follows the use of a solid core.

The annealed bundle of wire should now be made warm and basted with hot molten paraffin wax until fully saturated, then set aside to cool. Take off the rings, and unwind the binding wire ; at the same time wind on tightly one layer of paraffined tape. Then roll one turn of soft brown paper round the core and paste the edges. Paste the paper and roll on other turns until a tube of pasted brown paper is formed on the core to a thickness of $\frac{1}{16}$ in.

Whilst this is drying and getting firm, prepare two heads for the coil, or, regarding the core as the body of a bobbin on which the coil of wire is to be wound, prepare two heads for the bobbin. These heads may be made of mahogany, walnut, or other hardwood, or of ebonite. If made of wood, they should be soaked in melted paraffin to fill the pores. In shape they may be round, square, or octagonal, and if of wood, they should be 1 in. thick and 4 in. in diameter. If made of ebonite they may be a little thinner. Holes must be bored in the centre of these heads to exactly fit the ends of the core, and secured with good glue.

On this bobbin wind 4 lb. of No. 18 soft copper wire, double cotton covered and paraffined. First drill a small hole through one of the heads, close to the core, and push 8 in. of the wire through this hole. Then twist it round a pencil to form a spiral or helix. This end will be used for connecting the coil to other parts of the igniting apparatus. Wind on one layer evenly, then tie the last turn down with soft cotton, and well baste the turns of wire with melted paraffin. Proceed with the rest of the wire in the same manner, basting each layer as it is wound on. Finish winding at the opposite end to that of the commencement, taking the wire through a hole near the top of the head, and forming it into a helix. Baste the whole coil well with hot paraffin, and roll several folds of paraffined paper round the wire, smoothing down each fold with a hot iron. Then fit over the whole a cover of thin sheet ebonite, securing with a lacing of silk cord.

・ It is usual to mount a brass terminal or binding screw on each head, and to solder the ends of the coil to these terminals. They may be obtained from dealers in electrical sundries. Now make a groove in the surface of the head holding the commencing end of the wire, straighten the wire, and force it in this groove. Then lay bare the part to go under the base of the terminal, form it into a loop, fitting the tang of the pillar, and screw this down tight. The finishing end of the coil should be fixed to the other terminal in the same manner, and the grooves filled in with wax coloured to match the wood. If the coil is put in a protecting case, the terminals may be attached to the case, and then the helixes of wire will be useful in making the connections between the coil and the terminals.

Now, with two lengths of No. 18 wire, connect the coil to the two terminals of a 4-volt accumulator for a moment, when its core and coils will be charged with electricity. Then disconnect the coil suddenly, and note that this charge leaps across the air space between the end of the connecting wire and terminal (at the moment of disconnecting the coil from the accumulator) in the form of a bright spark or flash of light. It is this spark that fires or ignites the explosive mixture in a petrol motor, and the maker must arrange the make-and-break mechanism so as to break or disconnect the circuit in the combustion chamber at the moment of breaking contact, and therefore differs from the action of the trembler coil.

To make a compound primary and secondary coil with trembler break, proceed as for a plain primary coil, preparing the coil in the same manner, but this need only be 7 in. long. Bind the bundle of wires with one layer of paraffined tape as the rings and binding wire are being removed. Then warm a sheet of thin ebonite $\frac{1}{64}$ in. thick and 7 in. wide, roll it round the core firmly to form two folds, and fix the edge with Prout's elastic glue melted with a hot iron. This will form the bobbin body of the coil, to which must now be fitted two ebonite discs $3\frac{1}{2}$ in. in diameter and $\frac{3}{4}$ in. thick, securing them to the body with good shellac varnish.

The holes in the discs should be turned true and made to fit the ebonite sleeve on the core, so as to require very little varnish to hold them on. Also, one of the heads or discs must be pressed on over the core, so as to allow $\frac{3}{8}$-in. of the bare wire to protrude beyond the head to serve as an electro-magnet for the trembler arrangement. These ends should be free from tape and ebonite, and made level with a file.

When the bobbin, thus prepared, has set hard and firm, wind it first with the primary coil. Meanwhile prepare some sheets of paraffined paper in the following manner : Procure about eighteen sheets of good white demy paper free from specks and holes, ' each 22 in. by 18 in., examine each sheet by holding it up to the light and reject the faulty parts. Cut from these sheets of paper forty strips, each 9 in. by 6 in., to serve as insulators between the layers of wire, and sixty squares, each 6 in. by 5 in., for the condenser.

Next procure about 2 lb. of best solid paraffin
(paraffin wax), cut it into shreds, and melt it in
a square shallow tin baking dish, placed in a stew
pan containing water, kept hot over a fire. The
sheets of paper are to be passed through the
melted liquid paraffin with the aid of a pair of
wooden tongs, scraped over the edge of the dish
to free them from surplus wax, and hung on lines
near the fire to drain and dry. They are best
hung by small wire clips attached to one corner
of each sheet, and when cold, are ready for use.

The primary coil must be formed of soft No. 18
copper wire, double cotton covered, and previously soaked in the melted paraffin; a little over
½ lb. of wire will be required. First make a small
hole through the ebonite head which will hold the
trembler, close to the core. Pass 3 in. of the
primary wire through this hole, wrap one strip of
the paraffined paper round the core, carefully wind
on one layer of the primary wire with each turn
closely side by side, and secure the last turn with
soft cotton to hold the wire firmly whilst being
basted with hot paraffin. Then wrap another
strip of paraffined paper round the first layer and
wind on the next layer of wire, bringing the finishing end through another small hole in the same
head, but on the opposite side to the first. Then
secure the last turn with soft cotton. One of
these ends of the primary wire will be connected
to one foot of the trembler bridge, and the other
to a terminal fixed in the ebonite head.

Attention must now be paid to the shell of
ebonite between the primary and the secondary
coil. This is of great importance, as the length
and density of the spark from this coil depends
greatly on the perfection of insulation between
the primary and secondary coils.

Some coil builders adopt an almost perfect
method of insulation by having an ebonite tube
to form the shell. This may be done in the follow-

ing manner: Two small discs of ebonite are first fitted on the core to serve as bobbin ends to the primary. Then the larger heads for the coil are made to go over these, and fit an ebonite tube slid over the primary wire. This method requires a lathe to turn the parts, and also careful fitting.

The next best method with the coil under consideration is to get sheet ebonite $\frac{1}{64}$ in. thick, wide enough to just fit in between the bobbin heads, and long enough to form seven folds around the primary. Soften this in boiling water, and roll it whilst hot round a wooden roller slightly smaller than the primary coil. Then wind on enough tape to keep it in shape until cold. When cold, remove the tube and work its outside edge over the coil. Then stick the outside edge down with thick shellac varnish. Whilst the varnish is wet, wind on one layer of tape very tight, to bring the ebonite sheet in close contact with the primary wire, and allow it to remain until the varnish has set hard.

The secondary coil is formed of silk-covered No. 36 copper wire, which must be free from kinks and knots. If any of these faults are detected whilst winding, they must be cut out, the ends of the wire bared of its silk covering, the ends twisted together, rubbed with resin, and then soldered, after which they must be again covered with silk. Soldering fluid must not be used in soldering any part of a coil.

The quantity of wire required will be in proportion to the length of spark desired from the coil. Half-a-pound of No. 36 wire should yield a $\frac{1}{2}$-in. spark, $\frac{3}{4}$ lb. a $\frac{3}{4}$-in. spark, and 1 lb. a 1-in. spark in air, when wound over the primary previously described. The shorter spark will probably be sufficient to ignite the charge in a $3\frac{1}{2}$-h.p. petrol motor.

The bobbin with the primary coil must first be mounted on a suitable winder. Then one of the

strips of paraffined paper must be rolled round
the ebonite tube and smoothed down with a hot
iron. Next bore a small hole obliquely through
the edge of the left-hand head, and let it come
out close to the primary. Thrust a few inches of
No. 24 copper wire down this hole, bend up the
inner end to form a hook, and tie this firmly with
soft cotton. Then solder the commencing end of
the secondary wire to the hook thus formed, and
make the top portion into a helix for connecting
the inner part of the coil to a terminal. The bobbin of No. 36 wire should run freely on stout wire,
and be wound over the primary in the same direc-
tion as this is wound over the core. Each turn
must be wound on evenly side by side, and when
the first layer has been wound, it must be covered
with one and a half turns of paraffined paper
smoothed down as before. Then wind on another
layer in the same careful manner; but let it finish
with two turns of the head of the coil. Proceed
thus with each layer, winding and insulating as
at first, and bringing each a little short of the
heads, to prevent accidental sparking at these
points, with consequent ruin of the coil. The
vacant spaces may be filled with soft cotton
before putting on the next layer of paraffined
paper.

The winding must stop when the last layer has
reached the head opposite to that holding the
commencing wire, and the end of this layer must
be tied with soft cotton; about 6 in. should be
left free to form a helix for connecting to a terminal.

The whole should now be covered with paraffined paper, then with wide silk ribbon wound
on tightly, stitched down, and then the whole coil
soaked in melted paraffin until it ceases to give
out bubbles, when it may be taken out to drain
and cool.

A condenser must next be prepared to take

up the extra induced charge of electricity and give it to the secondary and sparking circuit, thus increasing the density of the sparks. This condenser is formed of fifty sheets of good tinfoil, each 6½ in. by 4 in., alternating with the sheets of paraffined paper already prepared. First lay one of these sheets on a smooth board, and drive four wire nails in at the corners to form a guide for laying the tinfoil. Lay the first sheet of tinfoil with the left-hand end protruding 1 in. over the paper, and the sides ½ in. in from the sides of the paper. Then lay another sheet of paper evenly with the first, and on it lay another sheet of tinfoil with the right-hand end projecting 1 in. over the paper. Thus lay each alternate sheet of paper and of tinfoil so as to have each alternate sheet of tinfoil overlapping

Fig. 95.—Diagram of Condenser Layers.

the paper at each end of the pile as shown in Fig. 95, where the dotted lines represent the paper and the thick lines the tinfoil. When all the sheets have thus been made into a pile, put two or three more sheets of paper on top, then a piece of blotting paper, and on this a heavy iron made warm enough to soften the pile, but not to make the paraffin run. When cold, roll it round two binders of paraffined silk ribbon to firmly bind the bundle. Next get two 6-in. lengths of No. 22 soft clean copper wire for connecting wires. Fix one of these to each end of the pile by rolling the projecting tinfoils around the wire, then stitching it in that position with No. 36 soft copper wire threaded through a darning needle.

The trembler arrangement for making and breaking the primary circuit consists of an electro-

magnet with its coils connected in series with
the battery and thus forming part of the primary
circuit. This electro-magnet is furnished with
an armature attached to a spring so arranged as
to form a loop of the circuit, capable of being
broken to form a gap when the current is switched
on to the coil. It is this breaking action of the
armature that gives the required spark from the
secondary coil, and, as this causes a momentary
cessation of current in the electro-magnet, it loses
its hold on the armature, which is drawn by its
spring back to close the gap, and complete the
circuit again. This action of breaking and closing the circuit is so rapid as to give it the

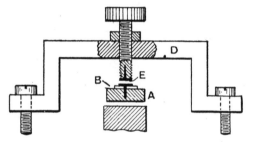

Fig. 96.—Longitudinal Sectional Elevation of Trembler.

appearance of trembling, hence the name of trembler being given to this part. The electro-magnet,
armature, and other parts, may be constructed
to form a separate instrument, and may be placed
in any part of the primary circuit. But it is
usual for compactness to construct it on one
head of the coil itself, the core of the coil serving
as the electro-magnet, arrangements for this having been made when forming the core and bobbin
of the coil.

The armature of the trembler A (Figs. 96 to
99) is a piece of iron bar $\frac{5}{8}$ in. in diameter and
$\frac{1}{4}$ in. thick. This is attached to one end of a strip
of hard German silver $\frac{3}{8}$ in. wide, $\frac{1}{32}$ in. thick,
and 2 in. long, by two short brass screws or rivets.

The other end of the strip B is pierced with a small square hole to fit over the top of a supporting pillar C, as shown in Fig. 97. When the armature spring is fixed to this pillar with a set screw, the armature must be exactly over the

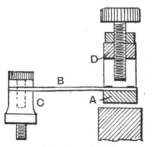

Fig. 97.—Transverse Sectional Elevation of Trembler.

centre of the core, with the two iron faces $\frac{1}{16}$ in. apart (see Figs. 96 and 97). In this position it is spanned by a bridge D, made with a strip of brass bent as shown in Fig. 96, with feet pierced with holes for fixing to the head of the coil, and a screwed hole in the centre over the armature to hold the contact screw. The trembler make-and-break will take place between the tip of this screw and the armature spring, and as sparks will occur when the circuit is broken, and these sparks will burn brass rapidly, the points of contact

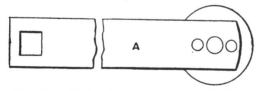

Fig. 98.—Plan of Armature and Spring.

must be protected with platinum. These points are best made with platinum wire No. 16 gauge. Drill a small hole $\frac{1}{4}$ in. up the tip of the contact screw, fit the platinum wire into this hole, cut it off, leaving $\frac{3}{16}$ in. projecting, and splay this over

the tip to form a rivet head E. Treat the lower
contact piece in a similar manner. As the current to work the coil will pass this spot, and as
the density of the sparks will be proportioned to
the density of the current passing here, these
contact points must fit each other with level
surfaces, so as to offer small resistance to the
current. One end of the primary coil will be
clipped under one of the feet of the break bridge,
and the other end to a separate terminal on the

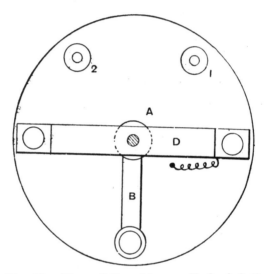

Fig. 99.—Plan of Trembler on End of Coil.

outer edge of the head as shown at 1 (Fig. 99).
This terminal will be connected to the battery,
and the other line from the battery will be connected to the break pillar.

The vibrations of the armature, and also the
character of the sparks, will be regulated by the
adjustment of the contact screw, which must
be fitted with a lock nut, as shown, to rigidly
secure such adjustments.

All the parts of the coil and condenser having
been prepared, they must now be put together.

The best made coils are all fitted with ebonite cases or cylinders, secured at the ends with ebonite covers made to screw on the ends and furnished with connecting terminals on the outside. In home-made coils a case can be made of hardwood well soaked in melted paraffin. If a rectangular case is prepared, the condenser may be first fixed in the bottom of the case, after having enclosed the connecting wires in india-rubber tubing, and brought the ends of both near the trembler end of the coil. The coil must then be fitted close to the condenser, and connected to it as shown in Fig. 100; that is, one wire from the condenser to the foot of the bridge, and the other to the foot

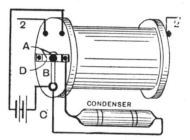

Fig. 100.—Diagram of Coil Connections.

of the break pillar c. Terminals may be fixed to the outside of the case, and short pieces of flexible cord made to connect these with the inside terminals.

If the coil is to be fitted into an octagonal wooden case, or into a cylindrical case of ebonite, it should be first enveloped in several turns of sheet ebonite to make sure of insulation between the secondary and condenser. Then the condenser should be warmed over a bottle of hot water and curved to its shape, and fitted to one side of the coil and bound with silk ribbon before being fitted in the case. In some 1-in. spark coils, insulation is made doubly sure by placing the coil and condenser into the case with the trembler part uppermost, and then filling up all spaces with melted paraffin.

When fitting the coil to its case, and this to the motor, pay special attention to the insulation of all connecting wires. They are best insulated when sheathed with rubber tubing. The terminals from the secondary coil must be kept at a distance from each other, and from other terminals or metal work, and their tangs must not be near the wire anywhere. The leading wires should not touch each other, or cross one another closely, nor rest against the coil or the condenser. Neglect of these precautions may cause leakage, and consequent failure in getting good sparks.

Fig. 101 is a diagram showing the method of working and the action of these two coils, A and B representing the cylinders of two motors. In A there is an ordinary sparking plug C attached to the secondary of a compound trembler coil D^1, the primary of which is in connection with a battery when the cam E closes the primary circuit by pressing together the two springs at F. Whilst they are thus pressed together the coil is excited, and a stream of sparks flow across the gap in the sparking plug, igniting the charge in the cylinder. In B there is a wipe plug G, consisting of a platinum-tipped rod and a platinum-faced spring. The rod works in an insulated stuffing-box, and its platinum tip is in contact with the spring (connected to the cylinder) when the cam H presses it into the cylinder. When the cam passes the tip of this rod, a helical spring J pulls it sharply away from the spring G, and, as the previous contact of these parts closed the circuit of the battery through the plain coil D^2, so this pulling-away action breaks contact and a flashing spark passes between the two separated parts at G. It must be noted that this spark only flashes across the gap between the separated parts at the moment of separation, or, in other words, "at the break," but not the "make" of the circuit. This must be taken into consideration when arranging the timing of the ignition, by adjusting the wiping cam. In A the sparking begins when the two springs at F are brought into contact, and continues whilst they are in contact; but in B there is only one flash when contact is broken. Sure ignition is ensured by the use of a compound coil with trembler attachment, but the timing of the

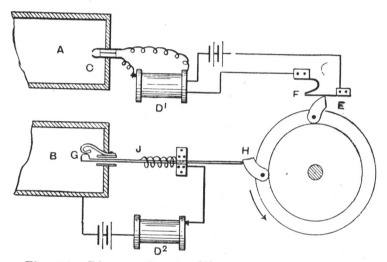

Fig. 101.—Diagram Showing Working of Ignition Coils.

ignition is said to be most correct with a plain coil.

In Fig. 101 the exact form of the parts, and position of the cams, has not been attempted, as the principal of the action only has been illustrated. However the cams may be formed or fixed, they should be made so as to be easily and quickly adjusted.

CHAPTER VII.

LIGHT-WEIGHT PETROL MOTOR FOR ATTACHMENT TO ROADSTER BICYCLE.

THE petrol motor to be described in this chapter weighs, with a 14-lb. flywheel, about 25 lb., which may be reduced by using a lighter flywheel. Thus

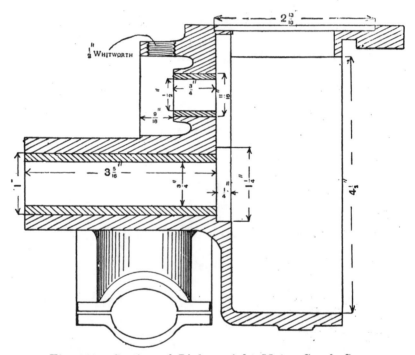

Fig. 102.—Section of Light-weight Motor Crank Case.

it will be specially adapted for fitting on to an ordinary roadster bicycle, whose front forks have been strengthened with tubular stays. Although the motor is light and simple in construction, nothing has been sacrificed to efficiency, strength, or bearing surface. It will develop $1\frac{1}{2}$ h.p., or, if very well made, should approach $1\frac{3}{4}$ h.p. The position for the engine is well up on the bottom tube, in a vertical position, thus enabling a long belt to be used, so as to grip the motor pulley. The main shaft bearing is $3\frac{5}{16}$ in. long by $\frac{3}{4}$ in. diameter, giving long life and steadiness in running. To complete the

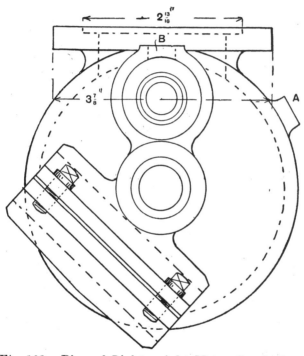

Fig. 103.—Plan of Light-weight Motor Crank Case.

engine from the rough castings a screw-cutting lathe of $4\frac{1}{2}$-in. or 5-in. centre is essential, in addition to the ordinary small tools of an engineer's workshop.

Specification.—One and a half h.p. air-cooled vertical engine. The lug which fastens it to the frame may be suitably fitted on the pattern for those who prefer an inclined position for the engine. Cylinder $2\frac{1}{2}$-in. bore by $2\frac{1}{2}$-in. stroke; outside flywheel, aluminium crank case; high tension electric ignition; spray carburettor of simple design; V-belt drive on the back wheel.

Crank Case.—The pattern for the crank case (Figs. 102 and 103) should be made with due allowance for shrinkage and machining. A corebox of rather a complicated pattern will be required to core the large interior, with depressions in the back of the case as shown for the two-to-one gear, for the hole through for the main bearing bush, and for the upper opening connecting the cylinder. The pattern may be made to leave its own core in the back of the case for the exhaust valve cam chamber. To machine the crank case, hold it by the main bearing extension in a three- or four-jaw chuck, and bore out the main bearing hole and the depression for the small gear wheel to the dimensions given in Fig. 102. Face the edge of the case, and true up its inside edge $\frac{1}{4}$ in. deep. If a suitable chuck is not available, the hole may be drilled halfway from each side, and the operations of truing up tne face and inside edge and recessing may be done on a mandrel between the lathe centres: but this will not make such a true job of it as if all the operations were done at one chucking. The hole for the main shaft bushing is 1 in. in diameter. The recess for the 16-tooth pinion is $\frac{1}{4}$ in. deep and $1\frac{1}{4}$ in. in diameter. The inside back of the case will not require machining, except at the two recessed parts for the 16-tooth pinion and the 32-tooth wheel. The 1-in. hole must be quite parallel, and if a 1-in. reamer is available, bore the hole $\frac{1}{64}$ in. under size and reamer out by hand in the vice.

Hole for Cam Shaft Bushing.—Next bore out the hole for the exhaust cam shaft bushing and the recess for the 32-tooth wheel; this should be $\frac{11}{16}$ in. in diameter and the recess $\frac{1}{4}$ in. deep by

2¼ in. in diameter. If the chuck is large enough, the casting may be set over till the hole runs true to perform this operation. If not, it may be done on an angle-plate bolted to the face-plate, the boring of this hole and the recessing being left until the top flange for the cylinder has been machined. Whichever way it is done, it

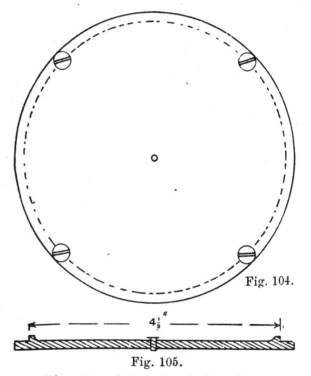

Fig. 104.

4½"

Fig. 105.

Figs. 104 and 105.—Crank Case Cover.

must first be marked out with its centre 1½ in. full from the centre of the main shaft hole. To do this, plug it with a piece of hardwood, mark off the 1½ in., and scribe a ¾-in. circle from this centre, and put centre-punch dots round this circle as a guide for setting and boring.

Machining Top Flange, etc.—To machine the top flange, fasten the casting to the angle-plate with a long bolt through the main-shaft hole, the trued-up face being on the plate. A piece of paper should be placed between this face and the angle-plate to avoid getting it dented or bruised, as this face and the trued-up inside edge must be kept perfect to ensure an oil-tight fit for the cover (Figs. 104 and 105). With the casting true, true up the face of the flange and the outside edge to $3\frac{7}{8}$ in. in diameter, and turn out the recess for the cylinder edge, $2\frac{13}{16}$ in. in diameter by a bare $\frac{1}{8}$ in. deep. Now bolt the casting to the machine up the back of the case. The cam shaft hole must be $\frac{3}{4}$ in. through, and the face for the cover (Figs. 106 and 107) for the exhaust cam chamber is $\frac{9}{16}$ in. from the edge of the cam-shaft bearing.

Advance Spark Apparatus.—If the advance sparking apparatus is to be purchased, it should be bought before the crank case is machined, some being small enough to work in the space here specified, while some are larger, and in this case a small recess must be turned in the top of the main bearing part. The cover (Figs. 106 and 107) will then not require the piece cut out of bottom, but will be quite circular. At this chucking, the face of the main shaft bearing may be trued up, so that its length from inside the face to outside is $3\frac{5}{16}$ in.

Assembling the Crank Case.—The clip holding the motor to the frame tube may next be bored to suit the tube. Roughly file up the faces of the two parts till they fit squarely together. Then mark off and drill for four $\frac{1}{4}$-in. or $\frac{5}{16}$-in. screws to hold the parts together, the holes being clearance in the bottom half and tapping in the top half. Bolt the two halves together, and bore them to size, either on the angle-plate in the lathe or on the drilling machine. To ensure a smooth, true hole, a bit or a reamer should be put through to finish. Remove the screws and file $\frac{1}{32}$ in. off

each to give the necessary clearance to allow the
clip to grip the tube. The pins may, if thought
necessary, be long enough to come through and
take a locknut. In tapping aluminium, use
paraffin as a lubricant, and do not allow much
swarf to accumulate in the flutes of the tap, or
the thread will tear up. Drill and tap a hole
at A (Fig. 103) to suit the oiling arrangement.
For injecting oil with an oil can a ¼-in. Whitworth thread, with a plain screwed plug, will
do; but for an oil pump worked from the saddle
a larger hole, to suit the particular connection
used, will be necessary. Another hole must be
drilled and tapped in the bottom of the case

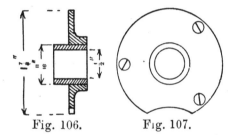

Fig. 106.   Fig. 107.

Figs. 106 and 107.—Cover for Exhaust Cam Chamber.

for letting out the waste oil, and this may be
fitted with a ¼-in. screw plug; but a small waste-
oil tap is handier and gives a better appearance.
The ½-in. Whitworth hole B (Fig. 103), to receive
the exhaust-valve lift-rod, must be left till after
the cylinder is fitted.

Crank-case Cover.—The crank-case cover may
now be turned and fitted to the case. A ⅜-in. lug
is left on the back by which to chuck it and to
form the air outlet. Only the edge and the part
which fits in and against the case will require
machining. It must be made an oil-tight fit by
being turned nearly to size and being then ground
in with powdered pumice-stone. It should be
left about ¹⁄₁₆ in. larger in diameter than the case,

and the edge should be milled to facilitate holding whilst grinding-in and for removal. The
cover is secured to the case by four $\frac{1}{8}$-in. screws,
as shown in Fig. 104. The cover must be chucked
again, back outwards, and the air-hole in the
centre formed. A flange should be left round
this, as shown in Fig. 105, so that the oil splashed
over the cover may run round the hole and down
again to the bottom of the case, instead of leak-
ing out on the outside. The hole may be $\frac{1}{16}$ in.
or larger, and the head of the flange $\frac{1}{4}$ in. in
diameter. A valve may be made of this if thought
desirable by fitting a $\frac{3}{16}$-in. cycle-ball, but it is
not necessary unless automatic lubrication is
fitted.

Small Cover.—The small cover (see Figs. 106
and 107) may be bored, turned on the edge to
$1\frac{7}{8}$ in., and faced on the inside. Bore the hole
for the bush $\frac{11}{16}$ in., and just true up the projecting edge. The piece is fastened to the case by
three $\frac{1}{8}$-in. screws with countersunk heads, as
these must not project beyond the face of the
cover.

Bushes.—The main bush of phosphor-bronze is
$3\frac{5}{16}$ in. long by 1 in. in diameter, with a $\frac{3}{4}$-in. hole.
Chuck the casting, bore the hole $\frac{1}{64}$ in. under size,
and finish with a 1-in. reamer. Knock the bush
on a tree mandrel, and turn it a tight fit for the
case, so that it requires driving in with a mallet.
A $\frac{1}{8}$-inch peg may be fitted half in the bush and
half in the case, $\frac{3}{8}$ in. deep, to prevent any possibility of the bush shifting. When the bush is
fitted, knock it on the mandrel again, and face
off the ends flush. Prepare the bushes for the
exhaust cam shaft in the same manner. The one
in the case is $\frac{3}{4}$ in. long by $\frac{11}{16}$ in. in diameter, with
a $\frac{1}{2}$-in. hole. The cover bush is $\frac{19}{32}$ in. by $\frac{11}{16}$ in.,
with a $\frac{1}{2}$-in. hole. Leave these holes a shade under
size, knock in the bushes, screw the cover in place,
and pass a $\frac{1}{2}$-in. reamer through both whilst in

position. Be sure the main bush hole is at right angles with the top flange face, the exhaust cam shaft hole parallel with the main bush hole, and

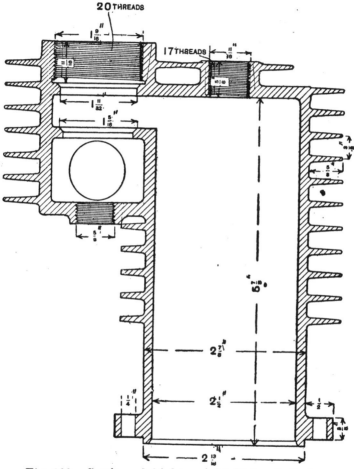

Fig. 108.—Section of Light-weight Motor Cylinder.

the hole in the tube-clip at right angles with the main shaft hole.

Cylinder Castings.—Dress up the cylinder castings, taking off all lumps and mould marks, level the bottom part that fits on the crank case square with the sides, and mark off. Plug a

piece of hardwood across the mouth of cylinder,
taking care not to drive it in too hard, and from
the edges of the cored hole find the centre. From
this describe with the dividers a circle $2\frac{1}{2}$ in. full
in diameter, and centre-dot lightly with about
eight dots at equal distances round the circle, as
a guide for boring. In a similar manner plug
the openings in the top of the cylinder for the
inlet valve and sparking plug, and mark off the
two openings so that their centres are exactly
$2\frac{5}{16}$ in. apart. As the finished sizes are $1\frac{9}{16}$ in.
and $\frac{11}{16}$ in. respectively, mark the circles about
$\frac{1}{16}$ in. larger, so that the guide marks will not be
obliterated in machining.   Drill the sparking-
plug hole $\frac{5}{8}$ in., to be ultimately tapped out $\frac{11}{16}$ in.
with seventeen threads to the inch to suit the
standard pattern De Dion plugs. If a tap to
suit this size and thread is not to hand, the
cylinder can be chucked on the face-plate and
screw cut to suit the sparking plug, but it must
not be threaded till the cylinder is bored, as the
plain $\frac{5}{8}$-in. hole will be required for a bearing and
guide for the boring bar. Face off the cylinder
top to a thickness of $\frac{5}{8}$ in. (see Fig. 108). Fig. 109
is a half plan of the cylinder head.

Boring the Cylinder.—To bore the cylinder,
bolt the casting truly on the saddle of the lathe.
It should be held firmly in position by two stout
iron straps bent to the radius of the cylinder, and
the casting should be packed up to the correct
height of the centres. See that everything is
quite firm and the lathe properly adjusted before
starting to bore, as on the accuracy of the work
on this part depends in a great measure the
efficiency of the engine. Take at least three cuts
through—four will be better—the finishing cut
being a mere scrape. The finishing cut and the
cut before it should be taken right through without a stop from start to finish, or a true bore will
not be obtained.

Making the Boring Bar.—The cylinder boring bar should be made from 1¼-in. or 1½-in. mild steel with one end turned down ⅝ in. to pass far enough through the hole in the top of the cylinder to allow the cutter to go to the top of the cylinder bore. This ⅝-in. part of the bar must fit the hole accurately, without shake from end to end. The

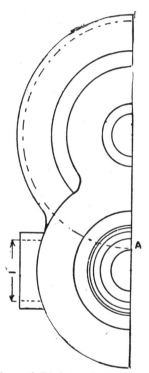

Fig. 109.—Half Plan of Light-weight Motor Cylinder Head.

bar, before being turned, should be drilled and countersunk at each end to the same angle as the lathe centres. Two cutters should be made, one for roughing and one for finishing, the latter to be used on the finishing cut only, and to be dead to size—namely, 2½ in. To make a perfect job the bore should be taken to about $\frac{1}{100}$ in. under size and reamed out by hand in the vice with a dead

parallel 2½-in. reamer, if this tool is already in
the possession of the worker. It will be an ex-
pensive tool to make or purchase, and would not
be economical unless a number of cylinders are
to be bored. A substitute may be a copper or
lead lap fed with flour emery and oil, but every
particle of emery must be washed from the work
with paraffin or petrol. If it is to be lapped out
the cylinder must be bored to within the merest
shade of the finished size.

Cylinder Flange, Shoulder, and Chamfer.—
The flange, shoulder, and chamfer on the mouth of
the cylinder may now be machined. The work
may be done at the same setting as the boring,

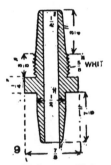

Fig. 110.—Exhaust Valve Guide.

by making cutters to fit the cutter bar, or it may
be done on a mandrel between the lathe centres.
To avoid making a mandrel the cutter bar may be
used, a collar being turned to fit tightly on the
⅝-in. part of the bar, and the outside may be
turned up in its place to·fit the bore of the cylinder. The small end of the bar can then be slipped
from the inside through the ⅝-in. hole and driven
with a carrier on this end. The flange should be
turned up true on both sides and left ⅜ in. thick,
and the shoulder should be turned 2¹³⁄₁₆ in. to fit
tightly the recess in the crank chamber. This part
should be a shade taper, so that the screws which
fasten it to the flange on the crank chamber will

pull it up tight. The diameter of the flange should be exactly the same as that of the crank-chamber flange. The mouth of the cylinder should be chamfered out as shown in Fig. 108 in order to facilitate the insertion of the piston and rings. *Boring Out Valve Chamber.*—The casting must now be chucked on the face-plate, head outwards, and fastened down with a bolt passing right through the sparking-plug hole, or held down by the flange with dogs or clamps. Get the dotted circle round the inlet valve opening quite true, and bore out and screw the hole for the exhaust-valve-guide (Fig. 110), $\frac{5}{8}$-in. Whitworth thread, and with a hook tool face the under side for the valve guide to bed truly against. Next bore the opening and seating for the exhaust valve to the sizes and angle shown in Fig. 108. The sides of the exhaust chamber should be cleared up with the hook tool. The opening and seating for the inlet valve may now be machined, and the top part bored out and screwed, as shown in Fig. 108. Face up the opening so that it is $\frac{11}{16}$ in. from the top of the valve seating. The casting must not shift during these operations, as it is imperative that the exhaust-valve seating, the screwed $\frac{5}{8}$-in. hole, and the under part for the exhaust-valve guide be absolutely true with each other, or the exhaust-valve will never be a gas-tight fit. It is well to rough the parts first, and then finally go over the above-mentioned parts with a light finishing cut to make sure they are true. The seating and screwed part for the inlet valve must also be dead true with each other. *Exhaust Pipe Opening.*—The opening for exhaust pipe, shown in the half plan of the cylinder top (Fig. 109), should now be bored or drilled out and tapped 1 in., with twenty-six threads to the inch. As it is rather light, take care not to burst this part in tapping. It is well to drill it out rather full, so that the tap works freely ; a

full thread is not necessary, as there is only the
weight of the exhaust silencer for it to support,
and this has a long bearing.

Clearance Holes for the Holding-down Pins.—
Next mark off the bottom of the cylinder flange
for six ¼-in. clearance holes for the holding-down
pins. Start the first hole to come at A (Fig. 109),
and mark off the other five equally from this.
Get the holes the correct distance from the edge
to allow the screw heads to clear the cylinder
wall, as there is not much space. The best form
of screw for the purpose has a square head with
a circular collar underneath.

Exhaust Valve Guides.—The guide for the
exhaust valve and the exhaust-valve push-rod
guide are shown in Figs. 110 and 111 respectively.

Fig. 111.—Exhaust Push-rod Guide.

The guide shown in Fig. 110 can be turned from
$\frac{15}{16}$ in. or 1-in. case-hardened mild steel, or from
tool steel hardened and tempered, or a pattern
can be made for this and for the push-rod guide,
and phosphor-bronze castings obtained. Whichever method is adopted the machining will be the
same. Drill the hole right through, a shade under
¼ in., and reamer it out to size. Turn up a mandrel to fit the hole tightly, and finish up the outside between the lathe centres. The shoulder may
be left round, and two or three ⅛-in. tommy holes
drilled in it, or it may be filed up hexagon; the
latter is preferable, as it can then be screwed up
tighter than with a tommy wrench. The push-
rod guide can be made in a similar manner, two
flats being filed on the base by which to screw it

up. To ensure the valve seating being true with the bore of the guide, a cutter bar may be made of ⅝-in. or ¾-in. mild steel with a leg turned down to fit the ¼-in. hole, a cutter being made to the size and shape of the valve opening and seating; this can be worked round with a lathe carrier by hand, and will make a true job.

Exhaust Valve.—The exhaust valve should be

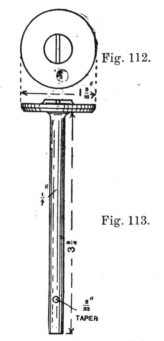

Fig. 112.

Fig. 113.

Figs. 112 and 113.—Exhaust Valve.

made to the dimensions given in Figs. 112 and 113. The head and stem are separate pieces screwed together, and the end is riveted over. The stem is a piece of ¾-in. mild steel having at one end $\frac{5}{16}$ in. of any convenient thread, the head being tapped to suit and countersunk. The stem is screwed in up to a shoulder and riveted over. The valve should now be truly centred at each end and turned to the sizes given in Figs. 112

and 113. The part to rest on the seating should
not be much more than $\frac{1}{16}$ in. wide, and of an
angle corresponding to that of the seating in the
valve chamber. The projection and saw-cut on
the head is for use when grinding the valve to its
seating with a screwdriver, or, better, a screwdriver held in a brace. The valve grinding should
be done with flour emery and oil, and may be
finished off with powdered pumice and oil after
all traces of the emery have been washed away.
The hole in the tail end of the valve stem should
be drilled $\frac{3}{32}$ in. and opened out to a slight taper.
It is for the pin to hold the valve spring up to
its work. It may be $\frac{9}{16}$ in. from the end, but the
exact position will depend on the length and

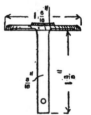

Fig. 114.—Inlet Valve.

strength of the spring used, and it will be best
to leave this hole till the valve and spring are
tied in their places.

Inlet Valve.—With the simple form of carburettor described on p. 99 the inlet valve will
be part of the carburettor, but should it be desired to fit any other form of spray or surface
type carburettor, then the inlet valve will be required of the size and form of Fig. 114. This
should be as light as possible consistent with the
work it has to do. The valve body (Figs. 115 and
116) is an iron casting, drilled $\frac{3}{16}$ in. and turned
to size. The valve must be ground to its seating
in the same way as the exhaust valve.

Inlet-Valve Spring.—The spring for this valve

is much weaker than the exhaust-valve spring, as the valve is opened by the suction of the downward stroke of the piston. The end of the spring is passed through the hole drilled in the valve stem, the position of this hole being left till the spring is tried in its place. It is best to buy these valve springs, as they cost only a few pence and are then certainly of a suitable strength. The correct adjustment of the inlet-valve spring is a very important matter, and can only be arrived at by trial. If the spring is too strong the valve will not open sufficiently to admit a full

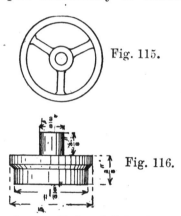

Fig. 115.

Fig. 116.

Figs. 115 and 116.—Body of Inlet Valve.

charge of gas, and if too weak it will not close quickly enough, and will thus cause loss of compression, and possibly back-firing.

Drilling Crank-Chamber Flange.—The cylinder can now be fitted on the crank chamber, and the holes marked off to correspond with the six ¼-in. holes in the cylinder flange. Place the cylinder on the crank case with the exhaust-valve guide directly over the centre of the exhaust-cam chamber on the crank case. Mark off through the holes in the cylinder flange with a scriber, remove the cylinder, centre-dot the crank-chamber flange carefully, drill $\frac{7}{32}$ in. bare, and tap to suit pins

$\frac{1}{4}$-in. Whitworth threads, using paraffin to lubricate the taps. The holes must be tapped carefully, or the metal will tear and spoil the thread. Remove the tap once or twice, and clear off the dust to avoid tearing. Then replace the cylinder, fasten it down with three screws, and with a long drill made to fit the bore of the exhaust-valve guide, drill the hole in the cam chamber for the push-rod guide. This will ensure the push-rod being exactly in line with the valve-stem. Tap it $\frac{1}{2}$-in. Whitworth to suit the guide, and screw it in place and test for truth. The push-rod will be a short length of steel turned to fit the guide freely, one end, operated by the cam, being rounded and hardened. The length must be arranged so that with $\frac{1}{32}$ in. between the rod and the valve stem the valve shuts down on its seating.

The Piston.—The piston is shown in section by Fig. 117, and in plan by Fig. 118. The hole for the gudgeon pin is $1\frac{1}{4}$ in. from the front of the piston. The ring grooves are $\frac{3}{16}$ in. wide by $\frac{1}{8}$ in. deep, and are $\frac{1}{8}$ in. apart. The distance apart of the faces of the bosses for the gudgeon pin is $1\frac{9}{32}$ in.; this is $\frac{1}{32}$ in. more than the length of the small end of the connecting-rod, a small amount of play being necessary here to prevent the piston binding in the cylinder. Of course, the play must be sideways only, the fit of the pin in the connecting-rod bearing simply allowing it to work quite freely. To attain a high speed with the least possible vibration, the piston, and, in fact, all reciprocating parts, such as the connecting-rod, should be as light as is possible consistent with strength. Hold the piston casting in the chuck by the lug cast on the head, and turn up the outside parallel to a working fit in the cylinder. Take a very fine finishing cut with a freshly ground tool and with a slow feed. When smoothed off with a very fine smooth file, the

piston should fit the cylinder so that if oiled it
will sustain its own weight. True up the bottom
edge, and turn a very narrow groove, $\frac{1}{32}$ in. deep,
$\frac{1}{16}$ in. from the edge, to facilitate lubrication.
The inside should be turned slightly taper as far
as the lugs, as shown, the thinnest part being left
$\frac{1}{16}$ in. full thick, and a rim should be left on the
inside $\frac{1}{8}$ in. bare thick, this strengthening the
edge somewhat. Face up the head to the lug by

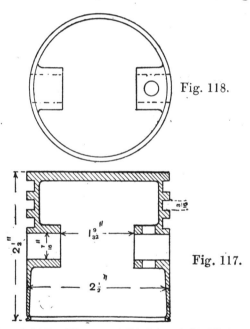

Fig. 118.

Fig. 117.

Figs. 117 and 118.—Piston of Light-weight Motor.

which the casting is held, leaving this part $\frac{1}{8}$ in.
thick. Then with a sharp-pointed tool mark a
light line round the centre, as a guide for drilling
the gudgeon-pin holes. Then carefully turn the
grooves for piston rings. To get them all alike,
make a tool, similar to a parting tool, just $\frac{3}{16}$ in.
wide and well backed off on each side for clearance. Any burr that may have been thrown up
should be carefully smoothed off, and the head

parted off with a long parting tool. Smooth off
the burr, and polish the head with several grades
of emery cloth. The more highly finished the head
of the sylinder the better, as the burnt gases will
then not so readily accumulate on it. If it is
held in the vice for polishing, great care must
be taken not to grip the thin edge, or it will get
cracked. Mark off on the centre line the positions
of the pin holes, which must be exactly opposite
each other. Drill a shade under the size, and then
hand-reamer the holes. In the absence of a reamer
the holes should be drilled with a twist drill to
finish. The best way to get these holes true is
first to drill halfway on tne lathe centre with a
small drill, say of $\frac{3}{16}$ in. diameter.

Facing Inside Faces of Bosses.—The inside

Fig. 119.—Gudgeon Pin for Piston.

faces of the bosses must now be tooled with a
facing cutter, the cutter bar fitting the hole without shake. The cutter is fitted to the bar, turned
up in place, hardened, and let down to a light
brown. To use it, pass the leg of the bar through
tne hole, and insert the cutter, and hold the cutter bar in the chuck with the back centre as
support and feed for the work. Drill a ¼-in.
clearance hole right through one boss, as shown
in Fig. 118, to hold the pin in place. One hole in
each lug would make a more certain job. The
face of the hole should be faced for the head of
the pin.

Gudgeon Pin.—The gudgeon pin (Fig. 119)
should be turned from ½-in. tool steel; it should
be quite parallel, and fit so as to require driving
into place with a mallet. Smooth it off to a high
finish, knock it in place, and through the hole in

the boss drill ¼-in. tapping size. Remove the pin and tap ¼-in. Whitworth, smooth off the burr, and harden, then polish and let down to a brown shade. Perhaps the easiest way to ensure the tapped hole coming exactly in line with the clearance hole is to knock the pin in place and drill to tapping size right through, then remove the pin, and open out the holes in the lug. When the pin is in place the ends should be clear of the face of the piston; for if level, or projecting in the slightest, the hard pin will mark the cylinder when working. The screw to keep the pin in place may have a cheese head with a screwdriver slot or a square head with a round collar under, similar to those used to fasten the cylinder to the crank case. The latter is better, as the pin should be a very tight fit to avoid any possibility

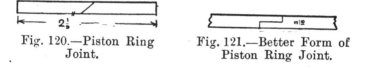

Fig. 120.—Piston Ring Joint. Fig. 121.—Better Form of Piston Ring Joint.

of its coming loose when working, but a box key will be required to screw it up with.

Piston Rings.—On the fit of these rings much depends, as if they are not perfectly fitted, loss of compression, and consequently loss of power, will result. There are several ways of making these rings, and the subject is sufficiently discussed in Chapter IV. (see pp. 57 to 59). A common method in cheap motors is simply to bore up a cylindrical casting, turn the outside to finished size, part the rings off the required width, and cut them through; but this is bad practice, as there is no spring in the rings to keep them up to their work in the cylinder. Make four rings whilst on the job, as it is very probable that one will be broken in finishing or springing on the piston, and even if not it is well to have a spare

ring. The rings should now be cut through (see
Figs. 120 and 121, and also p. 37). Before the
rings are cut through, they should be tried in
the piston grooves, and should go to the bottom
without shake. If there is any variation in the
width of the grooves, number the rings as fitted.
Should the rings require easing, place them on a
flat board and lightly smooth the sides with a very
fine smooth file, taking care to keep the file perfectly flat. Now, when the rings are cut, press
the joint together and try the ring in the groove,
and if it is too tight, ease a little off the insides
of the joint. They should be without shake, but
when the pressure is released the joint will spring

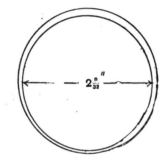

$2\frac{n}{32}''$

Fig. 122.—Piston Ring Bored Eccentrically.

open. With the rings all fitted and joints made
perfectly, they must be sprung together and
turned outside to $2\frac{1}{2}$ in. in diameter to fit the
cylinder bore (see p. 126). Before removing the
rings from the jig, try them in the cylinder, and
if they are a smooth-working fit within it they can
be removed and finally bored out to the finished
size, $2\frac{11}{32}$ in.; this boring will be eccentric with
the outside, as shown at Fig. 122, the thick
portion measuring $\frac{3}{32}$ in., and the thin part
$\frac{1}{16}$ in., being at the joint. The rings may
be held so that all are bored at one operation. Make a band clip, about $\frac{1}{8}$ in. narrower
than the combined width of the rings to be

bored, of sheet steel about $\frac{1}{16}$ in. or $\frac{3}{32}$ in. thick; clip the rings with the joints tight together, and hold them in a jaw chuck. The rings can be set true by the part of the ring beyond the surface of the clip. Bore with a fine-pointed sharp boring tool with a very light cut and feed. The rings are now finished, and may be sprung on over the head of the piston into place. This has to be done carefully, or a fractured ring will be the result. See that they do not stick in any part of the grooves; if they do, remove and carefully scrape the part to free it. With careful grooving and fitting, the rings should just drop down the grooves by their own weight, but without side shake.

Connecting-rod.—The connecting-rod (Figs. 123 and 124) can now be machined. Set the casting as true as possible, chuck the large end, and bore it out $\frac{3}{4}$ in. Chuck the small end, and bore it $\frac{5}{8}$ in. In chucking the small end, set it so that the two bores are parallel and with the centres $5\frac{3}{8}$ in. apart. It is usual in doing this work first to mark off the faces of the bosses on a level surface with a scribing block, and centre-dot the circles on these faces; but with the special set of castings designed for this motor, if the bosses are set true with the outsides, the bores will come exactly $5\frac{3}{8}$ in. apart without marking off. The phosphor-bronze bushes for the two ends may now be prepared. Chuck the large one, and bore and reamer it out $\frac{3}{8}$ in. The small bush is finished $\frac{7}{16}$ in. in diameter. Knock each bush on a true mandrel of the proper size, and turn the large one $\frac{3}{4}$ in. full and the small one $\frac{5}{8}$ in. full. They should be a very tight fit for their respective bores, as they are to be shrunk in place. Heat the boss of the connecting-rod to about the heat of a hot soldering iron, and knock the bush in quickly with a mallet, or press it in between the vice jaws, and cool at once in cold water. If this is properly

done, the bushes will never shift; but if thought
desirable, or if the bushes are found to be not
so tight a fit as was intended, a hole may be
drilled half in the bush and half in the boss, and
a small screw or peg may be driven in, and cut
off flush.   Now face off the sides on the mandrel in
the lathe centres to the dimensions given in
Fig. 123, leaving no more projecting on one side

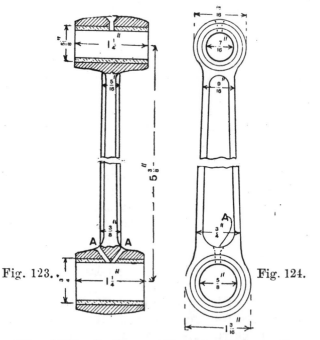

Fig. 123.   Fig. 124.

Figs. 123 and 124.—Section and Elevation of Connecting-rod.

than on the other.   Two oil holes should be
drilled in the large boss, as shown at A (Figs. 123
and 124), and well countersunk.   To facilitate
lubrication, file a small groove the whole length
of the bushes on the side where the holes pene-
trate.

   Setting Connecting-rod.—The connecting-rod
will now require careful setting. The mandrels

on which the bushes were turned should be inserted in the ends, and tested with the callipers to see whether the bores are parallel. The rod may be set cold if found out of truth. These mandrels should be made rather long, say 6 in. or 7 in., as, when used for setting, the extra

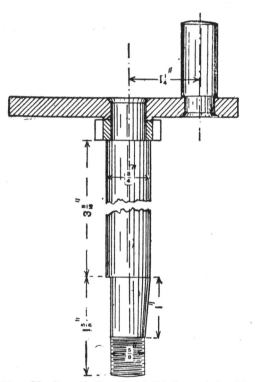

Fig. 125.—Shaft and Crank of Light-weight Motor.

length shows up any irregularity better. The bores of the bushes should certainly be reamered out to obtain a smooth parallel hole, the reamer being finally put through after the oil holes and grooves have been drilled and filed.

Main Axle.—The main axle should be made from a piece of tough mild steel, case-hardened, or of hardened tool steel ; the ends should be let down rather low, however, to avoid fracture, this treatment at the crank disc end extending to just beyond the pinion shoulder (see Fig. 125), and at the fly-wheel end to just beyond the end of the keyway. Let these parts down to a blue colour, the remainder or centre portion being left brown. A tool steel axle will wear longer unless the mild steel is very carefully case-hardened. Cut off a piece of steel $\frac{7}{8}$ in. or $\frac{13}{16}$ in. in diameter and $5\frac{11}{16}$ in. long. Centre, drill, and countersink each end to the same angle as the lathe centres, and turn the $\frac{3}{4}$-in. part to fit the $\frac{3}{4}$-in. reamered hole in the crank-case bush. A working fit without shake is needed. If the axle is to be ground after hardening, leave it large by $\frac{1}{64}$ in. bare for this. Grinding is decidedly preferable, as a perfectly true axle will result, but of course a good job can be made of it without grinding if a fit is made before it is hardened, and care is observed not to warp it in the hardening process. The end for the flywheel lock nuts may now be turned to $\frac{5}{8}$ in. for $\frac{5}{8}$ in. up, and then a line should be marked round the axle with a fine-pointed tool, 1 in. farther up or $1\frac{5}{8}$ in. from the end. Now set the slide-rest to turn a smooth taper that will start at this line and finish exactly at the end of the $\frac{5}{8}$-in. part. Reverse the carrier and turn down the other end $\frac{5}{8}$ in. $\frac{3}{4}$ in. up.

Securing Crank Disc and Flywheel.—The method of fastening the crank disc must now be decided. The plan shown in Fig. 125 is to make the axle end a driving fit through the small pinion and crank disc, countersink the outer side of the $\frac{5}{8}$-in. hole, and rivet the axle end up after a key or grub screw has been fitted right through the disc and pinion, half in the axle and half in the disc and pinion. If this is well done it will make a firm job, but for preference the hole in the disc and pinion should be tapped out $\frac{5}{8}$ in. by twenty-six threads, and the axle end screwed

to suit. With a right-hand thread the working of
the engine tends to screw it tighter, though if
desirable a grub screw may be fitted, but then
the pinion and disc must be screwed right home
before drilling for the grub screw. The other end
can now be screwed the same thread for the
flywheel lock nuts. The keyway for the flywheel
should be sunk 1 in. long by $\frac{5}{16}$ in. wide by $\frac{1}{8}$ in.
deep, but if this cannot be cut by machine, a
parallel keyway filed flat will be best.

Crank Disc.—The crank disc should now be

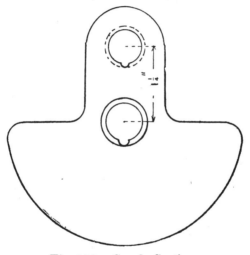

Fig. 126.—Crank Casting.

prepared. Find the centre of the axle boss, scribe
a line centrally on the crank-pin end of the disc,
and on this line mark off and centre-dot exactly
$1\frac{1}{4}$ in. from the centre of the disc for the crank
pin. Scribe a guide circle round these centre
marks a shade larger than the holes to be drilled,
and centre-dot these circles as a guide for drilling.
If a true drilling machine is available, these
holes may be drilled, using a $\frac{1}{8}$-in. or $\frac{3}{16}$-in. drill
first, and enlarging to the finished sizes, which
should be tapping sizes for $\frac{5}{8}$ in. by twenty-six

threads, left hand, respectively, if the screwed method of holding is adopted. In any case, to facilitate assembling, the crank pin should be screwed to the disc. Then tap these two holes. The crank casting is shown by Fig. 126.

Crank Pin.—For the crank pin, cut off a length of $1\frac{5}{8}$ in. of $\frac{3}{4}$-in. steel, and centre, drill, and countersink the axle. Regarding the material, the same remarks apply as for the main axle. Turn this up $\frac{5}{8}$ in. to fit the large end of the connecting-rod, round off an end, and turn down the other end to $\frac{1}{2}$ in. for $\frac{3}{8}$ in. up, and screw it to fit very tightly the tapped hole in the disc. This must be a left-hand thread. Provision must be made for screwing this home after the main axle and disc are in place in the crank case, by filing two flats on the outer end of the pin, or drilling a $\frac{1}{4}$-in. hole and drifting it out square for a key. The main axle and crank pin may now be hardened. Screw the pinion and crank disc on to the main axle the reverse way to the final position, that is, with the boss outwards. Face off this boss true in the lathe, so that the final combined thickness of the disc and boss is $\frac{3}{8}$ in., while at the same time the whole of the boss side of the disc may be turned up and the other boss for the crank pin faced off. Remove the disc from the axle, screw the crank pin into the disc, and turn the outer side of the disc. If the edges of the disc are now filed up, these parts will be finished.

Flywheel and Pulley.—The flywheel and pulley are in one casting (see Fig. 127). Chuck it by bolting to the face-plate, or by a three- or four-jawed chuck on the inside of the rim. Bore out the hole to the taper on the axle, the fit being tested with red-lead and oil smeared on the axle end, which should mark the hole from end to end and all round. If the lathe is true, the axle end may be finally ground in with fine emery and oil.

The edge of the flywheel, the pulley side, and the pulley can be turned at this chucking, if the casting is held in a jaw-chuck, or it can be roughed at this chucking, and finished in its place on the main axle, after the keyway has been cut, the key fitted, and nuts are screwed home. The latter method will be more likely to give the truer job. This key must touch on both sides from end to end, and should have a slight taper, the thicker end being towards the pulley side. The flywheel is 8 in. in diameter, with a rim $1\frac{1}{4}$ in. by $1\frac{1}{4}$ in. It may be lighter, but a heavy wheel gives a steadier running motor. The groove A, $\frac{3}{16}$ in. deep by $\frac{1}{8}$ in. wide, catches any oil which may leak out of the axle bearing, and thus prevents it working down the flywheel and splashing on to the rider. The pulley is $3\frac{1}{2}$ in. in diameter, and the belt groove is $\frac{9}{16}$ in. wide at the top by $\frac{1}{8}$ in. at the bottom, and the flywheel rim will require drilling with $\frac{5}{8}$-in. or $\frac{1}{2}$-in. holes to balance the piston and connecting-rod.

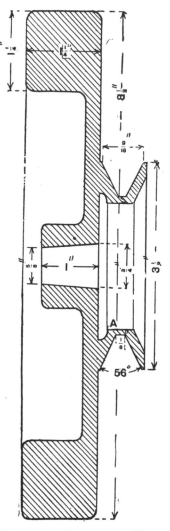

Fig. 127.—Section of Flywheel and Pulley.

Gear Wheels.—The two gear wheels to work the exhaust and ignition cams are phosphor-bronze

castings having thirty-two and sixteen teeth
respectively. The pinion is shown in section in
position on the main shaft in Fig. 125 (p. 141).
The larger one is shown in section on the exhaust
cam shaft in Fig. 128. If the teeth are cast they
may be filed to shape after the wheels are bored
and turned. The pinion may be tapped and
screwed on its shaft and turned in position. Only
just true the top of the teeth, face up the sides,
and scribe a fine line on both sides as a guide
for filing the bottoms of the teeth. The wheel

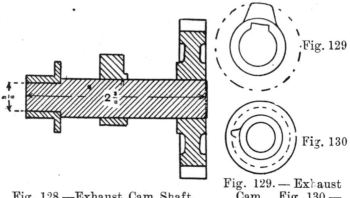

Fig. 128.—Exhaust Cam Shaft.

Fig. 129. — Exhaust
Cam. Fig. 130.—
Ignition Cam.

may be keyed on the exhaust cam shaft or screwed
on with a $\frac{7}{16}$-in. left-hand fine thread.

Exhaust Cam Shaft.—The exhaust cam shaft is
$2\frac{3}{8}$ in. long by $\frac{1}{2}$ in. in diameter, and is of tool
steel for preference, hardened and let down to
brown, the end screwed for the wheel being let
down to a blue colour. The other end may be
turned down $\frac{3}{8}$ in. for $\frac{7}{16}$ in. up to take the ignition cam, which may be fixed by drilling a $\frac{1}{16}$-in.
or $\frac{3}{32}$-in. hole right through both cam and shaft
while a small split pin to suit is passed through;
or the cam and the end of the shaft may be
threaded left-hand. The chief consideration in
screwing the ignition cam is the difficulty of

getting it right home to the shoulder on the shaft so that the cam is in the correct position for igniting; for this, turn a shade off the back of the cam until on trial it is found to come in the right position. Another method of fixing this cam is to make it with a ¼-in. square hole, filing the end of the shaft to suit, and allowing the end to project sufficiently to insert a small split pin. The exhaust cam is fixed by a plain flat key.

Exhaust and Ignition Cams.—The exhaust and ignition cams (see Figs. 129 and 130) should be turned from tool steel and filed or milled. The exact shape and size of the projection on the exhaust cam cannot be decided until the engine has been assembled and tested, which will be explained later in giving particulars of timing. The position of the exhaust cam on the shaft will be determined by slipping the shaft through its bearing in the crank case, with the thirty-two-tooth wheel screwed up tight. The cam must then come right up against the face of the bush so that there is no endshake to the shaft, but it must revolve freely. After the timing has been fixed, the cams should be hardened and let down to a brown colour. The ignition cam will require hardening only on the projection.

Timing the Exhaust Valve.—For this purpose partly assemble the motor parts. Connect the piston to the connecting-rod by the gudgeon-pin. Screw the thirty-two-tooth wheel to the exhaust shaft, place this in position in the crank case, key on the exhaust cam, put on the cover of the exhaust cam chamber, and place the main shaft in position with the small pinion and crank disc attached. Now carefully slip the cylinder over the piston without injuring the rings. Fix the cylinder to the crank case by two screws, and slip the crank pin through the large end of the connecting-rod and screw it into the crank disc. Insert the push rod into its guide, and put the exhaust valve with spring and cotter in place. Before going further, see that the exhaust stem is of such a length that there is $\frac{1}{32}$ in. play between its end and the top of the push rod when the valve is quite shut down on its seating. Now take a piece of $\frac{1}{4}$-in. or $\frac{3}{16}$-in. rod and, placing it through the sparking plug hole in the top of the cylinder, with the end resting on the top of the piston, mark off on the rod when the piston is at its highest and lowest positions. The wheels must now be in gear so that when the main shaft is turned forward (the way the engine will run) the exhaust valve will begin to open $\frac{3}{8}$ in. before the piston reaches its lowest point, and will shut exactly at the moment it reaches its highest point on the next upstroke. This can be seen by watching the marks on the rod passed through the top of the cylinder. When the right teeth are in gear mark them with a centre punch. The exhaust cam must be filed to bring it into the correct position.

The Ignition.—The ignition cam may now be fitted on the end of the shaft so that the projection is about one quarter of a revolution in advance of the exhaust cam. The advance sparking gear should be put on first; then the ignition cam should be so placed as to spark when the piston has $\frac{3}{4}$ in. to travel to complete its upward compression stroke for the earliest or most advanced sparking, and so that the spark will pass after the piston has descended $\frac{3}{4}$ in. for the latest or retarded sparking. The spark will pass at the plug points immediately on the break or coming apart of the platinum points of the trembler blade and screw. On the frame of the advance sparking apparatus and the edge of the exhaust cam chamber mark the " latest " and " earliest " positions, as guides when fitting the level and rod to work from the top tube of the bicycle. The advance sparking apparatus best suited to this motor is the small one of Bassée and Michel.

CHAPTER VIII.

SPRAY CARBURETTOR FOR LIGHT-WEIGHT MOTOR.

THIS simple and efficient carburettor, shown in section and elevation by Figs. 131 and 132, is of original design, and has been made and thoroughly tested; it would suit any motor of from 1½ h.p. to 2 h.p. It is fitted with a throttle valve and an extra air inlet, which have been found indispensable for successful and economical running. In fact, it is very difficult to keep the cylinder cool without these additions. For the motor described in the previous chapter this carburettor will be specially suitable. With it, the petrol tank can be fitted in the frame or behind the saddle. In fitting up the tank, it should be borne in mind that the bottom must be above the level of the petrol opening at the needle valve of the carburettor.

No special tools of any account are required to make the carburettor, a small lathe of 3-in. or 4-in. centres being all that is necessary; and if the operator is handy with a chaser, it need not be a screw-cutting lathe. Should the screwed parts which connect the top and bottom castings present any difficulty, an alternative method would be to make the screwed part a plain, tight, push fit, and to secure with three or four small screws put through the edge.

It will not pay to make the patterns unless several are to be made. Six of these are required. Should it be decided to make them, a core-box for the main body pattern will be necessary. Make the patterns as shown, allowing for shrinkage and machining.

Chuck the main body casting in a jaw chuck, and bore out the inside to $1\frac{1}{2}$ in. diameter up to the shoulder, which forms the valve seating; recess out the end $1\frac{9}{16}$ in. by $\frac{3}{32}$ in. deep. Bore the valve seating shoulder $1\frac{1}{8}$ in. Face off the end, and turn the outside of the bottom flange. Turn up a hardwood stud to fit the inside already bored, knock the casting on true, and bore out the other half of the casting $1\frac{1}{2}$ in. Face the valve

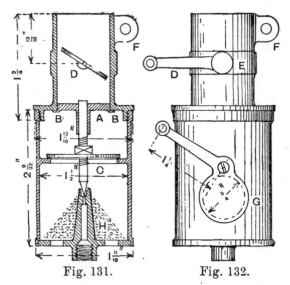

Fig. 131.   Fig. 132.

Figs. 131 and 132:—Section and Elevation of Spray
Carburettor for Light-weight Motor.

seating true, and face off the top edge; and, if the parts are to be screwed together, screw at this chucking with twenty-four to twenty-six threads to the inch, $\frac{1}{4}$ in. down the casting. Turn up the outside of the flange $1\frac{11}{16}$ in. If the lathe is not fitted with a three-or-four-jaw chuck, the casting may be knocked on a hardwood stud for the first operation as well as for the second. Chuck the top casting, large side outwards, bore up $\frac{7}{8}$ in. right through, turn out the inside of the large part $1\frac{3}{8}$ in. by $\frac{3}{16}$ in. deep, and screw or turn the outside to fit the main body casting, leaving the edge of the flange the same size as the flange on the main body casting—that is, $1\frac{11}{16}$ in. Turn up the remainder on a $\frac{7}{8}$-in. mandrel between the centres to the dimensions given.

Drill the small valve stem guide A (Fig. 133) $\frac{1}{8}$ in., and on a small stud running in the chuck turn up the small recesses shown at B (Fig. 131) on the ends to fit tight in the $\frac{7}{8}$-in. bore of the top casting. File up, and solder securely in place. Chuck the bottom plate casting with the long end, turn the edge of the plate to fit the recess in the body casting tight, and turn the sides until it is a shade thinner than the depth of the recess in the body casting; slightly chamfer the outside edge to allow of the edge of the body casting being riveted over to secure the bottom to the main body. Turn the short stem to $\frac{3}{8}$ in. diameter, and leave it $\frac{1}{4}$ in. long; drill up with a small drill for about $\frac{1}{4}$ in., remove from the chuck, and turn down the conical end $\frac{3}{8}$ in. at the base by $\frac{3}{16}$ in. at the summit by $\frac{7}{8}$ in. long. While in the lathe, mark a line $\frac{5}{16}$ in. from the edge for the centre of the holes to be drilled in the plate; these, six in number, are $\frac{7}{32}$ in. in diameter.

Knock on the bottom (but do not rivet it over yet), and secure the top part to the body. A drill must now be made with a $\frac{1}{8}$-in. shank, and the end turned down and formed into a $\frac{3}{64}$-in. drill. This drill will be 4 in. at least over all, but the $\frac{3}{64}$-in. part should be kept short to avoid spring, say $\frac{3}{8}$ in. The hole in the conical part of the bottom may now be truly started by passing the drill right through the top and valve stem guide while the bottom part is supported on the back centre. The hole will be $\frac{3}{8}$ in. deep of this size; the enlarged portions can be drilled on the centres when taken apart. The bottom end will be drilled and tapped to suit the size of the petrol regulating tap used. The remainder of this end up to the $\frac{3}{64}$-in. hole being $\frac{3}{32}$ in., the top end is also opened out this size for $\frac{1}{8}$ in. down. This may appear to be an elaborate method of drilling this portion, but it is quite necessary, as it must be perfectly true with the valve stem guide to ensure free and proper working of the needle valve.

The needle valve should now be made. The stem should be turned from a piece of $\frac{3}{16}$-in. steel. The finished size is $1\frac{7}{8}$ in. long by $\frac{1}{8}$ in. at the screwed part, the end being turned down to fit loosely the $\frac{3}{32}$-in. hole in the top of the conical part, terminating in a point of about 30°; the side of this stem where it enters the $\frac{3}{32}$-in. hole should have a flat filed on it to within $\frac{1}{16}$ in. of the point, to

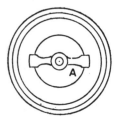

Fig. 133.—Valve Stem Guide of Spray Carburettor.

allow the petrol to flow by freely. The plate C (Fig. 131) should be drilled and tapped to fit the stem tight, a small lock-nut fitted, and then turned up in its place, $1\frac{1}{4}$ in. diameter by about $\frac{3}{64}$ in. thick. It should be fixed on its stem in such a position that when the needle valve is ground into its seat the plate will only barely touch its seating—that is, the plate resting on its seating must not prevent the needle valve closing the petrol inlet thoroughly, or the carburettor will flood and work irregularly. A saw-cut should be put in the head of the stem for a screwdriver to be used in grinding in the valve.

The throttle valve may next be finished. This is shown at D (Figs. 131, 132 and 134), and is for throttling or shutting off the amount of gas admitted to the cylinder. Drill a $\frac{3}{16}$-in. hole through the central collar E (Fig. 132), and turn up the small casting D (Fig. 134) to fit. The lever and stem, which are in one piece, pass through the main castings. The end which comes through may be screwed to receive a small nut or riveted over to secure it. The D section part of the stem which passes through should be filed so that the D section joins the round exactly at the sides of the $\frac{7}{8}$-in. hole—that is, the D part will be $\frac{7}{8}$ in. long. A $\frac{7}{8}$-in. disc of sheet brass, about No. 22 gauge, must be cut out truly circular to fit the bore of the body casting, this being slipped into

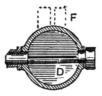

Fig. 134.—Section of Carburettor Throttle Stem.

place and secured to the stem by soldering or riveting. It must allow the lever to work freely, and yet close the $\frac{7}{8}$-in. opening when shut. It is not necessary that this should be a gas-tight fit when shut, but it should close the opening effectively.

When the lever of the throttle is at right angles to the perpendicular, the disc is not quite shut, this being provided for when filing the flat on the D section part of the stem. The reason for this is that correct movement of the operating lever on the machine is facilitated thereby. The end of lever D is drilled with a $\frac{1}{8}$-in. hole. The split lug F should be drilled to $\frac{1}{4}$-in. tapping size, one-half opened out to $\frac{1}{4}$-in. clearance and tapped $\frac{1}{4}$-in. Whitworth, the clearance side being faced level with a facing cutter. Saw through with a hack-saw

to just below the lug, and smooth off the "fraze."
The extra air inlet G (Fig. 132) should be drilled
¾ in. and faced off. The cover and lever should
be filed up and drilled, the end ⅛ in., and the pivot
hole the same ; it should be placed in position as
shown, and the position of the hole for the screw
marked off, drilled, and tapped to suit the thread
of the screw used. The ¾-in. opening may have
a very fine copper gauze disc soldered in to keep
out the dust.

The wire gauze cone H (Fig. 131) should now
be marked off and cut out as in Fig. 135, bent
to shape, soldered together at the edges, and
soldered all round the top and bottom edges to

Fig. 135.—Pattern for Gauze Cone.

the carburettor bottom before the latter is finally
riveted in place. In soldering the bottom edge
to the plate, care should be taken not to allow any
solder to fall on the part which rests on the recess
of the body, or it will not bed truly thereon, and
therefore the central hole in the conical part will
be thrown out of line with the valve stem guide.
A very light spiral spring (not shown) will be required, fitted between the cross-bar of A and the
top of the valve plate C. This quickens the action,
and ensures the needle valve remaining on its
seat when much vibration is set up. The carburettor will work without a spring in ordinary
circumstances, but it is better to fit one. The
strength may be arrived at by turning the carburettor upside down, with the spring in place, when

it should a little more than balance the weight of the valve.

A petrol regulating tap should be fitted to the bottom of the carburettor by screwing in with a leather washer between, to make a petrol-tight joint. This tap must fit well, and have a well-fitting washer, as petrol is very thin, and will work its way through the smallest aperture. A suitable tap for this purpose is one of French make of 2 millimètres bore, with connecting union. These can be obtained from almost any factor of motor fittings.

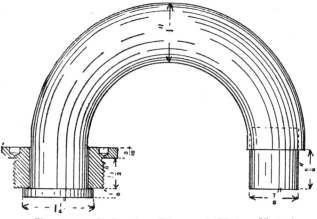

Fig. 136.—Induction Pipe and Union Nut.

The finish may be left in the brass, polished, or nickel-plated, as desired. A very nice finish may be obtained by having the body part dull-plated, and the small levers, screws, etc., plated and polished.

The connecting pipe (Fig. 136) will be a piece of 1-in. by No. 16 gauge steel cycle tube, about 9 in. long, bent to the desired shape. One end will fit into the top of the carburettor, being secured by tightening the pin of the split lug on the carburettor; to the other end is brazed a steel washer, 1¼ in. in diameter, with ⅞-in. bore and

$\frac{1}{8}$ in. thick. This must be faced and trued up on the edges. The union nut (Fig. 137) is made from a brass or gunmetal casting to the dimensions and shape shown in Figs. 136 and 137. The threaded portion is $1\frac{9}{16}$ in. by twenty threads to suit the "Work" motor, and the flange is filed up to a hexagon. Besides the hexagon for screwing up, it is advisable to drill three or four $\frac{1}{8}$-in. tommy holes in the top portion, so that if a large spanner is not available, a punch, or even a large

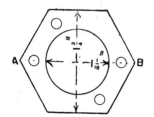

Fig. 137.—Plan of Union Nut.

nail, may be used to undo the nut should occasion arise on the road to have to take this off for repairs or adjustment.

A hole about $\frac{1}{16}$ in. diameter should be drilled in the top part of the induction pipe as near over the centre of the inlet valve as possible, for injecting paraffin to facilitate easy starting. This hole may be covered with a small spring oil-hole cover, as used on bicycle hubs. The section of the nut in Fig. 136 is through the line A B (Fig. 137).

INDEX

———◇———

PRINTED BY CASSELL & COMPANY, LIMITED, LUDGATE HILL, LONDON, E.C.